DATE DUE

GAYLORD			PRINTED IN U.S.A.

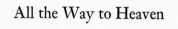

All the Way to Heaven

All the Way to Heaven

by Helen Caldwell Day

SHEED & WARD · NEW YORK

This book is dedicated to St. Catherine Labouré, who may be said to be the real foundress of the Catholic Union of the Sick in America, and to Our Lady, whose example we try to follow.

It is also for Father Meenan because of what he taught me about suffering, for the Foundress of the Catholic Union of the Sick in America, and for all members of CUSA all over the world.

Author's Note

The names used for actual living Cusans are, for the most part, fictitious. John Paul and others at the institution where he is are fictitious characters. They are not meant as a portrayal of any real persons, living or dead. And of course John Paul was never a member of CUSA: he is only a figment of my imagination—a Cusan who might have been but is not. Nevertheless the excerpts from group letters of the CUSA included in this book are actual excerpts from real book-letters, exchanged between the members and used here with the permission of the respective group leaders and our CUSA foundress; and the facts about Cusans other than John Paul are all true as here recorded.

Grateful acknowledgment is made to all the group leaders in CUSA who permitted me to use quotes from their group letters and who helped me in other ways to prepare this book; also to our National Chaplain, Rev. Father Finn of Palmer, Massachusetts; to our General Leader, Mrs. Robert Brunner; and to the Secretary of CUSA, Miss Grace M. Gavin, for her help in selection and editing, and especially for her encouragement. Thanks also are due to Miss Angela Lazzari of Blessed Martin House for her help.

FOREWORD

When Helen Caldwell Day proposed, a year ago, to write a book about our Catholic Union of the Sick in America, I was very happy. Now that her dream has become a reality, I see with great joy that she has succeeded in expressing, in a very lively manner, what is the very essence of our organization.

The experiences of John Paul, who represents the typical Cusan, are so real, so representative of those dear people who come to CUSA to find there consolation, courage and spiritual help, that many Cusans will probably be reading their own stories in his.

Like John Paul, the chronically sick have two heavy crosses to bear; first of all, there is the depressing feeling of being useless members of the community, leading purposeless lives. Everything they have been dreaming of—a beloved profession, vocation to marriage or the religious life, even simple social life—has been denied them, for many without any hope of return. Others less gravely stricken are still allowed a certain activity, but will have as constant companions fatigue and frequent relapses. They all experience in their lives what is one of the conditions of admission to CUSA: "A state of health that is an occasion of sacrifice." And it is here that the CUSA miracle works: those who never heard of it, as well as those who had at least a theoretical knowledge of the Doctrine of the Mystical Body of Christ, will find that in this tenet of our Faith lies the answer to their frustration and the sense of futility in their lives as invalids. They will come to understand fully and with deep joy the most important truth that CUSA aims to teach them, as it is expressed by their first motto: "We suffer for a purpose."

As one of our chaplains once said: "The Cusan must embrace the whole world with his love." Is it not marvellous that one helpless invalid here in the United States, offering lovingly his cross, may save souls of Communists in Russia or China, be the means of sanctification for unknown priests and laymen, help to bring light and contrition to many sinners and unbelievers? Here is realized fully the promise of our Lord Jesus: "By your patience you will bear fruit."

How uplifting is this conviction that his life is precious, to the invalid confined to his room! . . . Oh! The beauty of the Dogma of the Communion of the Saints that unites not only all the members of the Church on earth but even in Eternity.

The second cross of the chronically sick is their isolation. In many ways, they do not any longer belong to the world of the healthy—they feel that it is difficult for their family and friends, even when very loving and attentive, to understand their problems. However, in their little CUSA family, they will find understanding, love and—better still—many examples of simple, cheerful, even heroic, courage in the same difficulties. For they are often quite gay, despite their hard life, our Cusans; many are even full of serene spiritual joy; most of them come to be more attentive to the sufferings of others than to their own troubles.

When one member of a group passes through a period of conflict, of depression, how lovingly do the others hasten to encourage with kind words and the promise of prayers.

The second motto of CUSA, "A brother helped by his brother is like a strong city," has become a living reality.

Who better than Helen Caldwell Day, who is the excellent leader of one of our groups, could understand and make the reader see all that is to be found in that companionship of the Cusans? As a nurse she had, before her own sickness, learned to understand the problems and handicaps of the sick. In her first book, *Color Ebony*, she made us realize to what point she had experienced in her life, and in many ways, the sufferings of body, heart and soul.

Her patient acceptance and offering of her crosses have borne magnificent fruit in her foundation of Blessed Martin House, where she lives in daily contact with poverty, rejection and suffering of the most acute kinds. She has depicted that life in her second book, *Not Without Tears*.

Now, in this new book, she has really shown her art in making the reader breathe the atmosphere of CUSA life. Cusans will recognize themselves here, and they will, with us, wish that many other sick and handicapped may, owing to this book, be attracted to come to us, hoping to find in our CUSA the answer to their problems.

May your readers be many, dear Helen, and receive your message with a loving comprehension. May your book bring anew hope to the afflicted but also be read by healthy people, so as to make them understand the value of the role of the sick they encounter.

We are deeply grateful to you and hope that many souls will be called by the Lord, like yours and all true Cusans', to understand as did St. Thérèse of the Child Jesus, the International Patron of CUSA, that their role in the Church is to be the heart that suffers and immolates itself so that Divine Love may be better known and loved by many souls that will glorify God during all Eternity.

LAURE BRUNNER

ix

CONTENTS

I.   Darkness

There was darkness outside and darkness in him as he stared out of the open window at the pavement brooding below under the dim street light, with little rivulets of water still marking a trail down the walk to the sewers, a lonely sound. The pain was there too, in him, but then the pain was always there; one learned to live with it—after a fashion. The worst was the helplessness, the dependence, the emptiness, of a life that mocked him, living that had no meaning, no purpose, that held no promise but continued only because he had no power to do anything else but live. His lips twisted upward in an ugly grimace that was not a smile, but a caricature of all smiles people who suffer joyfully smile through pain. He looked down at his legs, shrunken and useless, and at the hands idle, almost bloodless, lying on the arms of his wheel chair, useless, as they had always been, as they would always be. He had not, he thought bitterly, even the power to destroy himself.

And he was ashamed of himself immediately, he did not know why. Someone who knew him little might have said it was his faith, he was a Catholic, but he knew it was not that: he had long since ceased to live by faith, if he ever had. Perhaps, long ago, when he was a child. . . . He did not know. It mattered little now.

1

Not that he rejected his faith altogether; no, it was not that either; it was just one thing more that meant little in days that meant nothing. A chaplain came to the "Place" (he always thought of it like that—"the Place"—his mind trembling over that other, uglier word, "institution," he hated, and refusing to form it) once a month, and now and then he went to confession and Communion when asked if he wanted to go. A few times he had even been to Mass, when some thoughtful person had come to wheel him over.

He knew it was a hard job, he was so very helpless, so he hated to ask it of anyone, though he was grateful when anyone offered to take him. It put something in days that were meaningless, in an existence that seemed purposeless, like a mistake the Creator had made and forgot to erase. He hoped that soon He would erase it by putting an end to an existence that never had had a reason to be. And the hope that it would be erased soon was a fervent one. It was the oldest hope he remembered—and there were so few things worth remembering in all those years since that day, nearly twenty-five years ago, when that unknown mother, whom he hated with quiet loathing, had left him, a blanket-wrapped baby of about a year, on the steps of an orphans' home, with a note that said his name was John Paul and he was a Catholic.

They had not kept him at the orphans' home because of his hands and arms—he could not use his hands and arms. They only took normal children. Then he had been able to use his legs and feet a little. However, a fall a few years later had further damaged his spine until now he could only move his head and neck. Since he was six he had spent his life in bed, or in wheel chairs when he was feeling his best—almost twenty years of helplessness and pain and dependence on others for his smallest needs. Twenty years is a long time. The state paid orderlies, doctors, nurses, technicians and therapists, dieticians and other personnel to care for him, and others like him, hopelessly crippled in body or in mind, there at the Place. Those who were crippled in mind were in another building, but he saw some of them at long intervals, and sometimes pitied them and sometimes envied them their vacancy. They lived in false worlds, but their worlds to them were real and had some meaning, while his did not. Despite all its care and expense the state could not give him, nor the others, the one thing their life craved, an answer, a meaning to being.

A Catholic chaplain came once a month to hear confessions and bring Communion to those who wished it, just as other chaplains of other faiths came also once a month to minister to people of those faiths. And all were kind and good men, friendly and easy to talk to. The chaplains came oftener too, if necessary, to administer to the dying or those in danger of death. But they were busy men, and though full of cheer and encouragement, none had been able to answer for him the questions of his own existence. "God works in mysterious ways," one said, and another, "Some day we will understand these terrible things that now are a mystery, like suffering. But now the answer is not clear. Remember though, your suffering is nothing to our Lord's. He suffered more than any of us and bore it patiently. We must expect suffering and bear our sufferings patiently."

He took no comfort in these answers, and found no meaning there. That far off "some day" was too remote, too uncertain and indistinct. He needed an answer now, he had to live now. But had no reason to live, just the necessity to live because he still breathed and his heart beat. And, yes, he knew Christ had suffered, but His suffering had been for a reason. Besides, He was God, "And

3

I am not," he thought rebelliously. "What has that to do with me? I am not God."

An orderly interrupted his thoughts to bring his dinner to him and get him ready for bed. The work on this particular ward was hard, and many of the orderlies did not want to work there because the men could not help themselves at all.

"Lifting all them heavy guys around like they was babies, putting diapers on them and feeding them. The hell with it! Why should I break my back for a guy that never will be no good nohow?" He had heard them sometimes, outdoors, downstairs under the window where they had gone out for a few minutes to smoke cigarettes.

"Okay, John Paul," the orderly said cheerfully, "time to eat supper and turn in." He picked John Paul up out of the wheel chair easily, as if he had been a child; John Paul was not very big.

"God, you're getting heavy! You keep eating the way you do and I'm gonna have to lift you up with pulleys. Whatever is wrong with your arms and legs sure hasn't hurt your stomach none, has it?" He continued talking as he pushed the tray table up in the bed and rolled the bed up until John Paul was in a sitting position. Deftly he shoved a spoonful of the steaming soup into John Paul's mouth. It was too hot. John Paul spat it out with a grimace.

"Watch it—" the orderly began angrily, then cut himself off, seeing John Paul's expression. "Oh hot, eh? Sorry, buddy, it's been up from the kitchen a long time and I thought it was cool by now. How about some meat?" He cut a piece of meat and raised it to John Paul's mouth, which he opened obediently to receive the food while the

4

orderly rambled on conversationally. "Yep, you can eat, can't you? That's one thing you guys up here can sure do. Outside we gotta pay tax on bread and soap and beer and smokes and everything else they can figure to lay a tax on so they can build more and more places like this and keep 'em for guys like you who lie and eat and stare out the windows like you was doing when I come in, at nothin'. I can't understand it, can you? I'm not griping, ya understand. I know you gotta eat too, but I sure do wonder what it all adds up to, sometimes; where it makes sense."

The orderly shook his head puzzledly, as he carefully spooned another mouthful of vegetables into his charge's mouth. He did not mean to be unkind. He was just one of that thoughtless mob that make up so much of the untrained help in such institutions for the crippled or the insane. The state paid him to give care, not love, to its charges, because love is not a thing that can be bought and paid for. He had a job and he did it as well as he knew how. He simply did not realize the cruelty of his words nor the pain he inflicted.

John Paul choked on the food but made himself swallow it. "No more," he managed to say above the spasm of choking.

"Oh, got enough, huh?" the orderly went on cheerfully, carefully wiping his patient's mouth and offering him a drink of water. "Not so hungry tonight, huh? Oh well, that is because you don't get any real exercise. Your appetite is funny. Sometimes you feel like eating, sometimes you don't. Now me, I work so hard my back's breaking, and I'm so hungry by the time I get a chance to eat, I can eat a cow, anytime. I mean I can really go to it. My wife's always saying I work too hard, but a man, a real man, has to work hard,

I tells her all the time. A man's work and his religion, that's all a man is, I always say."

The orderly took the dishes away, washed his patient's hands and face, and turned the dim light on. He made all the other preparations that were a part of getting John Paul ready for the night, caring for his more intimate needs with the quick, sure hand of experience that was gentle as well. At last he was finished and went away. When he had gone, John Paul lay awake, thinking, for a long time. One phrase kept running over and over in his tired mind, "a man's work and his religion, that's all a man is." He had neither. He was nothing. Nothing.

It was the next morning when Miss Grey, one of the nurses, brought him the booklet that was to change so many things for him, although of course he did not know it then. He could see it was something about Christmas. A Christmas message for some sick people, the Catholic Union of the Sick in America, or CUSA as they were more popularly known. He read while she held it open for him. He knew then that she was trying to cheer him for the coming holiday which had long ceased to mean anything to him. But he liked her. She was his friend, almost the only real friend he had ever had.

Long ago when he had been a child, there had been another, a woman who had loved him and mothered him, an attendant who gave those things one is not paid to give—interest, affection, love. For three years she had been his light. Then she had married and gone away to start a home, a family of her own. For a long time, years, she had still come back to see him, and even now sometimes she still wrote to him, but it was a long time, nearly two years, since he had received a letter. She had her own children now, and she was very busy. Since then, there had been no one that mattered until Miss Grey had come, because he had mattered to no one. Often he had wondered why he mattered to her. One day an attendant told him that she had had a crippled brother who had killed himself. Then he understood. He thought this was why the thought of self-destruction, that sudden temptation, had shamed him. It would hurt Miss Grey. He looked at the Christmas booklet she had brought him to read and read the first page where she opened it:

"Jesus' Birthday

"Dear Little Jesus,

"Happy Birthday to You. All I can give You is my thanks and my love.

"Thank You, dear God, for becoming man and suffering and dying for us so that we might live in heaven.

"Thank You, Jesus, for letting me be a cripple, so that I may suffer and thereby help some soul to get to heaven."

"Oh God," he thought, "a nut. Just the thing a woman would like, a woman would write." He read it all. It was signed by a man: Jerry Filan.

He could not understand it. The man must be nuts or must not be very badly crippled, he decided; no one who really suffered could have written like that. He was not sure he wanted to read any more—still, she was his friend. He did not want to hurt her feelings. He would read a little more to please her, he decided.

"Turn the page, please," he asked, and she did so, smiling at him. His eyes skipped over some lines and were caught by others:

". . . We sick people are always poor in some way, poor in strength, worldly pleasures and joys, miserable very often by the monotony, the helplessness, the continuous pain, the isolation, the solitude. How many hours sick people have to struggle through in mental and physical anguish, and if

7

victorious in that struggle, if able to keep smiling, there is no danger of losing the value of it through our pride! The struggle was too hard, the experience of the inner weakness, impatience, nervousness, too humiliating to leave room for vain thoughts. Have you not all experienced this?"

Had he not experienced it! If he could have moved his hands, he would have buried his face in them, to hide what he felt, but he could not hide the wound she had opened from Miss Grey because a tear spilled over, of which he was ashamed. She was kind and pretended not to see. He would have asked her not to make him read any more, but he was curious now. This writer knew something of suffering!

"But there is something marvelous about these sad appearances, and so it is one of the blessings of the CUSA to make us conscious of the possible beauty of our seemingly poor lives: We suffer for a purpose, and so let us say 'Sursum corda,' for if we sow with tears in our eyes, other souls will reap the fruits of salvation and sanctification."

Beauty in his life? That was a wholly new concept, one not even suggested by that long line of chaplains who had come and gone. Purpose, yes. They had tried to make him see some hidden purpose, but the hiddenness angered him. He did not believe now that there could be beauty or joy, though this writer suggested both. Sursum corda indeed! How could he lift up his heart when it had long since died but just continued to beat stubbornly? He longed to be able to tell that unknown writer what real ignoble, helpless suffering was like. He said so.

"She already knows," Miss Grey said soberly. "She also has been bedridden twenty years, or almost so. Yet she says 'Sursum corda.' I don't know how."

He could not believe it. How could there be any joy or beauty in such meaningless, fruitless suffering as his?

Pregnant suffering of childbirth he could understand; necessary suffering for healing, that made sense; but this—this agony of a useless existence that was worse than the pain of it—what was beautiful about it, or fruitful or even sane and reasonable?

He demanded the answer imperiously, not knowing that behind the intensity of his words there was a plea, a seeking for meaning and hope sounding through the reserve which he had always worn to protect himself, which Miss Grey caught and put on paper. It was this plea that the general leader of CUSA answered a few weeks later in a shaky, funny little hand which was so characteristic, and which was to grow so dear to him in the years to come.

II.   CUSA

It was not long before John Paul received an answer to his letter to the general leader. There were several small leaflets enclosed. One told something of the organization itself, and the other about qualifications for membership.

Miss Grey read it to him:

N.B.

"The Catholic Union of the Sick was started in a sanatorium in Switzerland in 1914 by a very fervent French Catholic, Louis Peyrot. His promising career as a medical student had been cut short by illness. He did not let this conquer his spirit, but he joined a group of the sick, the 'Coccinelles,' founded by Adele Kamm, a Protestant girl, whose members aimed to encourage and help each other by friendly group letters. However, gradually he began to see even greater possibilities for such a group if the members were united not only naturally, in a spirit of friendship and helpfulness, but supernaturally as well, as members of the Mystical Body of Christ; united in suffering, in sharing the Passion of the Head and offering their sufferings with His.

"With this in mind, he had started a group of Catholics, somewhat on the organizational basis of the Coccinelles but in another spirit. He wanted the members to recognize that the secret of happiness is to do God's will in doing for others. This latter seems impossible to those helpless and in great pain, yet it actually is not, since they can offer their suffering for the good of others. He wanted them to realize in their lives the doctrine of the Communion of the Saints; that the Church is one, and that we all suffer or all glory together, each member contributing in God's plan to the health and good of the whole Mystical Body. This was the incentive to sacrifice the group was offered and gladly accepted."

At that point, John Paul made Miss Grey stop reading. He had to think about that. "Read the rest later," he mumbled.

Miss Grey smiled and did not press him but gathered the friendly letter and leaflets and went away.

"Sure, John Paul," she told him, as she was going. "I know you must be tired. How about taking a little nap now, and later, after I have my lunch, I'll come back and take you for a ride around the block? Maybe we'll even stop for a cold glass of beer if we have time."

That would be a real and rare treat for John Paul. No one else had ever thought of anything like that before Miss Grey had come. When others took him for a little ride—which was rare indeed—they bought him milk and ice cream or malt. So did Miss Grey most of the time, but one day she had said to him, "Say, John, how would you like a real man's drink for a change? You're grown up to be quite a man now, you know." She had turned to the man at the counter. "Give us two beers, nice and cold."

"Okay," the counterman had answered, and in a moment had brought back two full frosted glasses of beer. "Bottoms up," he had said.

After the first experimental sip, John Paul had loved it,

and drank deeply in cool mouthfuls while Miss Grey held the glass to his lips.

Afterwards she had laughed and said, "Now you are a real roughneck. How does it feel? Here . . ." She wiped his mouth on his sleeve. "That's how the prizefighters do it."

John Paul had laughed too. He had been so happy. Oh yes, Miss Grey knew how it was with people like him; she knew how other folks felt and how to make them happy.

That reasoning made his mind come back to CUSA. Since she was so right about other things, maybe she was right about this too. He couldn't see it now, not as she saw it; but it did make some sense the way she was reading it and explaining it. It needed thinking over, but there could be a lot to it.

That day his legs hurt him dreadfully. At times it felt as if every separate nerve of his limbs was drawn tight and throbbing with tension. An unexpected shower had poured down torrents of water outside, so he knew he couldn't have his walk after all. He didn't really care very much though; he was hurting too much to care—everything was pain. Maybe it was the dampness, or maybe the lack of exercise—he had been so depressed of late that when the therapists came he yelled at them crossly and they shortened the time of his exercise. They were tired and busy and there were other patients to be helped who were more cheerful and less trouble.

Now he was sorry and ashamed because he knew some of the pain was his own fault. And in the midst of his pain he was tortured again by thoughts of futility and hopelessness that threatened to engulf him in the blackest despair.

That is the way Miss Grey found him when she came to bring him a hot drink later and some vitamins. In something like panic, he asked her to read him "more about that group when you have time."

She promised, and as soon as she could she came back and read more. She read about the spread of the group from Switzerland to Germany, France, Belgium, Italy, Canada and, finally, the United States, in December 1947, by the efforts of a woman coming from Belgium. In 1933, the Holy See had formally recognized the importance and validity of the group in its French branch (UCM) and CUSA received the papal benediction, the then Cardinal Paccelli giving the most enthusiastic praise to this work being done by the Catholic Union of the Sick, the work of offering suffering in a spirit of prayer and charity.

This amazed John Paul, and he listened closely as she read the requirements for membership. He thought they must be very strict and hard if it meant so much that even the Holy Father thought it was important. Maybe he was not good enough.

The requirements for membership were few. Miss Grey read: (1) one must be a practicing Catholic and (2) one must be in a state of health which offers the occasion for sacrifice. He breathed a sigh of relief. He was eligible after all, then, to try. One could become better; one need not be a saint to start off.

She went on reading more about the organization. The members were in groups of eight, each with a leader, liaison officer and chaplain. They corresponded with one another by means of little booklets known as the group letter. In these they wrote, each one after the other according to the order of the mailing list, the leader beginning, the others following. In the middle of the list was the liaison officer, who took care of some little administrative details. The chaplain ended the list, so as to be able to answer all, and from him the booklets went back to the leader to start another round.

Each group had its own special patron, motto and intention. Miss Grey read him some of the intentions: "the conversion of the Communists," "the conversion of our country," "the peace of the world," "the sanctification of priests"; and some of the mottoes: "We suffer for a purpose"; "*Sursum corda*"; "One sows, another reaps"; and "Pray, pray much."

The groups were made up of men and women in different localities and circumstances and backgrounds, united in suffering and sharing each other's burdens, sorrows, joys and sufferings in a spirit of charity, and not only each other's but all the world's.

There were dues of $2.00 a year, but the leaflet explained that lack of these should not hinder anyone from membership.

At this point, Miss Grey offered to take care of his dues for him if he decided to join.

"I have already decided," John Paul told her. "I want to join if they will have me." He knew he could lose nothing, and it promised wonderful things. He was so tired of life as he had known it, that day-upon-day of suffering that seemed to be without meaning—and indeed, sometimes, without end. There must be more for him than this; maybe here at last he could find that meaning to his life. Maybe he did have something to offer the world, after all; certainly he did, if suffering was something one could offer. His life surely gave him many "occasions of sacrifice." Maybe in this group he could help himself answer the question of his own existence.

Miss Grey wrote the letter of application, telling his name, age, diagnosis and condition, his interests and a few other things about him. Then they both went down to mail the letter, John Paul in a wheel chair pushed by Miss Grey.

14

Afterwards they began to wait and count the days for an answer.

The few weeks seemed to pass very slowly, crawling along like a broken wheel chair. Yet each day held an expectancy which had not been there before because of what each day might bring. Now that he had definitely made up his mind to become a Cusan, it seemed to him that he could not wait to be assigned to a group. While they waited, Miss Grey read him more from the 1948 Christmas newsletter which had first caught his interest. He especially liked the chaplain's message. At first Father Finn (the first chaplain of the American CUSA and sort of general chaplain) told how Mrs. Brunner of New York had wanted to start in America the counterpart of the European union of the sick, having seen its work as Catholic Action in Belgium and France. Then he also told of its founding originally by Louis Peyrot, who had seen the great possibilities for Catholics in such an organization because of the high spiritual motives born of the Church's doctrines of the Communion of Saints and the Mystical Body of Christ that could be brought to bear on it.

"This is highly important," Father Finn said. "There are existing societies and groups to aid the shut-ins, exchange ideas or hobbies, swapping books and pictures, etc. They are good in their way, in aiding the sick, giving them new material interests to take up their time. But this idea is different. It is to bring home to them that they are not just isolated wrecks of humanity, helpless to do anything, who are to be waited on by others and in whom often a little selfishness is induced by this fact that they are always to be served.

"For them to realize that they have a part to play in God's world, a very important part of Catholic Action, that they can do something for the world to make others happy and the world better, which the active and well often can not do, will be a great lift to their morale. It will give them an objective in life that will in turn redound to their own physical, mental and spiritual health. If they can be brought to realize that they can do for others something of what the contemplative cloistered orders do by prayer and sacrifice, even as a small group, it will add greatly to their joy and give them an enthusiasm that will carry them beyond four walls of a sick room.

"If they can come to grasp Newman's thought and apply it to themselves in the 'Communion of Saints,' life's a stage whereon we play a part—some high, some low: but what counts is not the part we play but how we play it before God. . . ."

So he had a part too, an important part, if one could believe this Cusan chaplain, a part he even compared to that of the contemplatives, that wonderful group of God's picked troups.

When Miss Grey had first come she had brought Thomas Merton's *Seven Storey Mountain* and it had fascinated him. These were real heroes, he had thought, these quiet men who passed their lives in silence, prayer and work for the glory and honor of God, and did it so joyfully. But he would never have dared compare his life with theirs, not for a moment. They had chosen, heroically, their state; his had been forced on him. It had never occurred to him before that, by accepting his in a more generous manner, he too was choosing it, and he too could offer it.

While she had been reading him Merton's book, on the contrary, he had tried to imagine himself different, strong and healthy with brown arms and legs, and muscles that stood up when he flexed them. He had imagined himself working in fields under a sun that made him sweat and browned him like the earth. (He had difficulty here, because he had never seen a field, nor even a garden, just pictures in books. He couldn't imagine the smell of hay or the sound of the farm machinery.) And then his eyes had fallen on the shapeless helplessness of his own limbs and he had been ashamed of his dream. He would never walk in brown fields under the sun nor rise at dawn to sing God's praises in a choir. He would just sit here helpless forever.

Father Finn's words stirred his imagination again though. Now he saw his bed as a cell and the long hospital grounds as a cloister. All his life of suffering was suddenly an offering of sacrifice caught up in that other sacrifice and given to God. He was the priest and this was his Mass, the sacrifice of his life, of himself. The idea exalted him and fanned the flames of imagination higher. The world was the congregation and he gave of his sacrifice to it.

Then he stopped, for he was afraid of pride. Perhaps all of this was presumption, after all.

Still he was happy, and not even the orderly's talkativeness could diminish it. He tried to sing a little, under his breath, in that funny, cracked voice of his, and did not mind when the orderly, George, smiled.

At last the day came when the waiting was over. He received a letter from CUSA headquarters saying that he had been accepted and was assigned to Group V, where Jerry Filan, the first American Cusan, was the leader. He could expect to receive the group letter soon, and they hoped he would be happy in CUSA.

John Paul was very happy, and Miss Grey seemed hardly less so. She busied herself about the room singing, and seemed not a bit surprised but pleased when he joined her, way off key. She said instead, with a smile of approval, "Isn't it wonderful, John! I am so glad for you."

III.   New Friends

John Paul received the first group letter with joy and eagerly waited for Miss Grey to read it to him and so to introduce to him his new friends. There was Jerry Filan, Claire Morgan, Lorenzo Clifford, Margie Malley, Florence Mills, Lucille Olivak and Father C., besides himself.

As leader, Jerry Filan had the first letter. He began by explaining the meaning and purpose of CUSA and introduced the members and their ailments or handicaps to each other. Then he introduced himself:

"I was born with spastic paralysis in 1918. I could not walk when I was a child. However, I kept improving until the winter of 1935-36. At that time I could take four steps alone, stand up, dress myself and do many other things alone. I was never perfect, however, and my mother talked about taking me to Lourdes some time when we could afford it. In April 1936 I took a turn for the worse. I am now completely helpless. I can't even sit up alone. I can't eat solid foods or even go to the bathroom naturally. After Mother died in 1943, my sister Mary told me we would go to Lourdes as soon as the war was over. There is no medical cure for me and no doctor can tell why I got so bad in the last ten years. Mary and I believe that if God is going to cure me it will be at Lourdes.

18

"Later I will tell you all about our first trip to Lourdes. We hope to go back again. My friend is writing this for me now because I cannot write very well. I hope God and His mother bless the trip. I only want to be cured if God wants it that way. Of course, I would like to be cured so I won't be a burden to anyone. I don't want to get better just to get rid of suffering. Suffering is the only way to get into heaven. I want to get better so I can help people and do good work for God."

Then Jerry explained to them more of the spirit and workings of the organization, little details which were not included in the CUSA circulars but which helped immeasurably to build up a family spirit and to assure the smooth functioning of each group as a unit.

"The letter is not to be kept more than three days," he explained. "This is to insure a speedy round for each letter, so that interest is held in the subject discussed. When the letter makes the round too slowly, the members of the group are likely to become discouraged in the value of our apostolate or lose interest in it.

"Each person should put at the end of his letter the date received and the date sent. Then mail to the next person on our mailing list. At the top of your letter put the page number, and your number on the mailing list—for instance, my letter would start 1/1, second page 1/2, and so on. The leader is first on the mailing list and the chaplain last.

"Enclosures of pictures, and so forth, may be included in the letters, but we should be considerate and practical in this and not send too many, because of the added postage and bulk. If you do not have a stamp, you will find extra ones in the small cellophane envelopes pasted on the back of our mailing list. Help yourself to what you need. If you have an extra stamp, you can enclose it in that envelope.

19

"We try to write about six pages if we can. If the letters are too short, they are difficult to answer sometimes because there is nothing to grasp. If they are too long, again we have the added bulk and postage. Let's try to keep our letters this length.

"Be sure to use the special envelopes which you have all received by now for mailing our group letters. You will notice the return address is that of headquarters. This is to make the letters easier to trace if lost in mailing. Do not put your return address on the outside of the letter.

"The group letters travel from coast to coast and north to south, even up to the English-speaking part of Canada. Cusans have generally shown that they prefer this arrangement, even if it delays the round somewhat, because the variety of location makes for more interest in the group's conversation.

"You should notify a member of your family or a friend of your membership in CUSA and tell them to whom to send the group letter in case you are too ill or otherwise prevented from writing it or sending it out.

"I think that is all. From time to time, I will include other pointers like this which experience at headquarters has shown to be effective in CUSA for smooth functioning."

Claire's letter was next. She was blind and spoke a lot about her seeing-eye dog after her greetings to the others.

"In 1948 I went in training for a seeing-eye dog named Vicky. At that time she was seventeen months old and mostly resembled two large ears with four oversized paws —ribs and a light coat of tan in between. Our month's training was full of hard work, fun, and finally a rewarding sense of accomplishment. The day Vicky and I embarked on our new life together was not unlike a wedding day—

a union of trust, purpose and a common desire to love and serve.

"However, we unsuspecting 'new owners' have lots to learn. Not all our experiences are noble (though most are), for some are humorous and others a wee bit embarrassing. I'd like to tell you a few amusing adventures my girl and I have had.

"When lost one day in a completely unfamiliar neighborhood, I told my dog to find someone from whom we could ask directions. I followed the tugs on my dog's harness—ah! here was a store. I walked in to find myself in a local bar! After getting directions, we made a hasty retreat.

"We board a bus and sit behind the driver. Vicky feels this is her seat, she gets more air and a few extra pats from passengers. One day we took the Fifth Avenue bus and Vicky just stood still and wouldn't budge. I suspected our seat was occupied, so I told her to go down the aisle. However, the man sprang up and said, 'Here, have my seat! That dog stared me out of it.'

"Vicky and I had a wonderful trip to New York Saturday. I had to go to Pambrock Pemberton's office and was interviewed by a reporter from the *New York Post*. Vicky was the first seeing-eye dog permitted to enter a New York theater. The *Post* did a story on it and took pictures that night as I was entering the theater, while inside and on the stage. The play was 'Harvey' . . . and delightful it was. Vicky enjoyed it too. Now seeing-eye dogs will be admitted to New York theaters. Up till now they have been refused admittance. Vicky's good behavior, plus fine cooperation, has made it possible for other students with dogs to get into theaters to see plays and musicals. I am engaged to a wonderful man, Michael Bradford. He is starting his instructions this week. I am hoping that while the priest is instructing him in our Faith, he will want to embrace it. We are hoping to marry soon, and it would be so wonderful if he could become a Catholic. Your prayers will mean so much and I will be sincerely grateful for them."

Florence Mills wrote:

"How happy I am to meet such wonderful people! And how I hope that I may measure up to all that is expected of the members of CUSA. I am not ill—perhaps for that reason I do not really belong to this select group. The only thing that gets me under the wire is the loss of all the sound the world produces. I am deaf—completely and totally deaf—since 1939.

"One of you mentions the need of humility in illness or physical handicaps. It is not a very pretty quality in human nature that looks down on those having less than normal of physical gifts, but it is a quality we must look for and accept as graciously as we can.

"Looking back on those years in which I had to accustom myself to being *different*, I realize that it took me a long time to accept the fact of physical inferiority, and to build my own world in which I found peace.

"*How much importance we attach to what others think and feel about us!* Detachment needed!

"I think deafness is the most estranging of all infirmities. Hearing is the social sense, and when it is lost one is cut off from mental contact with others and lives in isolated silence. There are, of course, substitute means of communication, but the hearing world is seldom patient or tolerant with substitutes.

"The important thing, it seems to me, is to build up or fortify self-respect, and after that, to look for all possible compensations through which to gain the respect of one's associates.

22

"For the past three years, I have acted as audiometrist, social worker, lipreading teacher, back patter and general morale builder for the Apostolate for the Deaf and Hard of Hearing of our diocese here. Our offices are housed in the Catholic Charities building. This building holds samples of all the heartaches of this immense city of New York and all other cities. I am doing some work now with the Negro deaf and hard of hearing—going up to Harlem once a week in the wintertime.

"I don't know if my various experiences connected with my work would be interesting to you, so I'll wait until I know before talking about them.

"I am particularly pleased to see the contentment expressed in our first letters, for I know that whatever the circumstances, we can create our own world and find happiness. Of course, one doesn't achieve that mental attitude overnight, and strong faith and confidence in the Providence of God are a necessary foundation for the slow building of happiness within the restrictions imposed by a handicap. And I can see that our members have successfully adjusted themselves to the inevitable. I have met our general leader, a most compassionate, zealous woman. Her work for CUSA will live long after her.

N.B.

"I am planning a trip out west to my home town and will let our leader know of my whereabouts so the letters won't be held up on my account. My days are filled to the brim with work, work, work.

"Now I know you will excuse me, the job is waiting. Please know how happy I am to meet you all."

Lorenzo, forty-five years old, suffered from arthritis. He said:

"My hobby is reading. I like mystery and Pearl S. Buck. I also like sports, especially baseball. The Red Socks are my team. I belong to two book clubs and I am having a hard time to keep up with them. Since I had a bad spell this summer, it had left me either lazy or I have something in my system that hasn't cleared up yet. I have had times in my illness when I thought I would go out of my mind with pain that I never got a moment's rest from. But we have to pray that God will give us the patience to live with it."

That was all the letters. Margie, Lucille and Father C. followed John Paul on the mailing list, so their letters would be in on the next round. Each letter also had special notes to the other members included and sometimes in these a little more about the writer. For instance, in his letter Jerry told John Paul and Lorenzo: "We are very alike in our crosses, so I'm sure the little Jesus will smile on us and help us to bear our sufferings well and encourage each other." And in her letter Claire explained that she had suffered also from tuberculosis and a heart disease.

Lorenzo added, "My problem is finding ways to use time. Back in 1938 I was free of pain and I started a magazine agency and selling cards. Jerry, you seem to be carrying a very heavy load, but I'm sure God will eventually make things easier to bear. Even in our helpless way we are doing something worthwhile. I'd love to get to know all the members by photo and would like it if we could all manage to exchange a picture. I think it would be nice. How about it?"

When Miss Grey had finished, she asked him how he liked his new friends and family.

John Paul smiled a big, real smile. "Swell," he answered. "Just swell! But gosh, you know they all make me ashamed. The way I've been feeling and acting . . . that Jerry Filan especially. What he must suffer! I hope Jerry will tell us more about his trip to Lourdes and that he will get to go again."

"Oh, I'll bet he will," Miss Grey guessed. "No one could forget a trip like that, I'll bet. It is probably the biggest thing that ever happened to him. Now tell me, do you want to answer the letters now or would you rather think about them a little while first—and maybe answer them in the morning?"

"I think I'll wait till in the morning, if you don't mind, Miss Grey. I want to think about it a little while first."

"Yes, I think that's best too," the nurse replied. "I'll see you later then, John Paul." She took the letters and left the room, turning once to smile at him.

In a little while the orderly came to give him his dinner. "Well, well, and how's tricks today, John Paul?" he greeted him.

"Just fine, George, thanks." John Paul smiled.

"Well, that's fine," the orderly responded genially. "How's about staying up and eating in your chair for a change today?"

"Okay," John Paul said.

"That pretty little nurse certainly is a whiz, ain't she? A real Florence Nightingale. She takes up a lot of time with you fellows that she don't have to, just on her own. You all sure should be grateful."

"I reckon we are, George. You don't find many like her."

"You sure as hell don't. She's a wonder. I reckon the reason for it's simple though. You know, she once had a brother like you, all crippled up, hopeless. They say they were pretty close; she was crazy about him. Then he killed himself. Couldn't take it, I guess. I know just how he felt. I couldn't take it either, I don't think. I'd rather be dead

25

than laid up, just living, no use to myself and nobody else, good for nothing."

John Paul was thoughtful, thinking about Jerry and Claire and the others. "I don't know, George. It sure is tough sometimes. And you wonder where you're going or if you are ever going to get there. But I guess it's all in the way you look at it, really. Maybe we cripples are really doing something good for you normal folks whose health we wish we had, just by being what we are."

The orderly was immediately and genuinely sorry for the hurt he thought he had inflicted. "Oh, I didn't mean it like that, John Paul, honestly. Nothing personal. I know we have to take care of you, no matter how helpless you are and God is pleased. He sure wouldn't like it if we just let you starve and die. Course, them of you as has folks is just as dear to them folks as if you had two good arms and legs. They are that grateful to have you alive. And then, if it wasn't for folks like you, I wouldn't have a job, so I sure ain't kicking, 'cause I like to eat well as the next one.

"What I meant was just that I wouldn't want to be a burden on nobody, myself, that's all. Folks are different. Me, I'm too independent. Like to do for myself. And I'm a man; I've got a wife and kids. If I can't take care of them, I don't want them to take care of me. It's the man's place to do that. I just wouldn't feel right if I couldn't. I'd rather have it over with. When you're dead you don't feel nothing and it don't matter what happens."

"It might be good if we could be sure it was that simple," John Paul dissented. "But we don't know that. If there is a heaven and a hell—and brother, I believe there is—we sure as hell are going to feel a lot when we're dead, good or bad, depending. It's funny too, it may be not only depending on ourselves, but depending a little bit, or a lot sometimes, on somebody's sufferings we didn't even know."

He hadn't known he was going to say all that. A few weeks ago he had been wondering if death didn't hold the answer and release, any sort of death, even of one's own choosing, a voluntary act. Now he knew differently. Then he would have been ashamed to call himself a cripple, he could not have formed the words to say it. But now he had said it, and he was glad. And that about suffering had been pure inspiration, from Jerry's letter and Louis Peyrot and the others. Maybe he would make a good Cusan after all. Maybe he could understand and offer after all.

Now he could plan his letter in the group letter, because now he felt like one of them too. He closed his eyes. What would he say? How would he start?

"Dear new Family,

"I enjoyed reading all of your letters so far and look forward to the others. You all seem to have so much courage and patience while I have not. But I hope I can learn.

"Jerry, yes I am a spastic too, though not as bad as you. Please tell me more about yourself, since we have the same trouble. And tell us all about your trip to Lourdes. That must have been really wonderful. I have never been outside this institution overnight, and rarely at all except just around the block. It must be wonderful to have a real family to love and care for you. I never had a family but I have two wonderful friends, Miss Grey who is my nurse and writes for me, and who told me about CUSA, and there was one other, an attendant, who used to care for me long ago and who was like a mother to me. Miss Grey is teaching me a lot about myself and my faith. I had forgotten most of it, though as she talks now it brings a lot to my mind of what my other friend used to say. But I didn't understand at all then, I was so young. The she could not express it as well as Miss Grey.

"Miss Mills, I think you are wonderful to make your handicap a means of helping others similarly afflicted. It must make your life richer to know you are able to be of great service to others. I'll ask the Little Flower to help you in your busy days.

"One of our orderlies here is always talking about the burden we cripples are to others, and sometimes it makes us think we really are of no use in the world. That is why I could hardly believe it when Miss Grey first tried to tell me about CUSA. I did not know I could help others just by being what I am, offering it to God. That sure makes you think, doesn't it? And everything looks different. Otherwise daily annoyances like this make life almost impossible.

N.B.

"Claire, Vicky sounds like a wonderful dog. I know many people will be grateful to her and to you for making the way smooth for them to go to plays too.

"Sincerely your friend,

"John Paul Jones

"P.S. Just call me John Paul. Everybody does."

When he finished the letter in his head, he smiled again, and with his eyes still closed, drifted off to sleep.

IV.   *Ubi Caritas*

It seemed a long time to John Paul before the next group letter came—months. Really only a little over six weeks had passed since he mailed the group letter when Miss Grey brought the second group letter to him.

"Know what this is, John Paul?" she asked as she held up the big brown envelope for him to see. Already he recognized the envelope which would grow more and more dear and familiar. "It's my letter!" he exclaimed. "I do hope you have time to read it to me."

"I came in for that very purpose," she assured him, and taking a chair, moved it closer to his wheel chair and sat down beside him.

"The first letter is from Lucille Olivak," she said, and read: "Hi, folks. Gosh, you all write such grand letters— I enjoyed them so much. And they bring me new hope and faith for the future too. I am badly crippled from contracted nerves since six years of age. I live with my mom and dad and she is wonderful. My hobby is collecting hankies and writing poetry. Do you feel the call of SPRING? It is everywhere here on Cozyhill. The jonquils in their golden loveliness. Now it will be great to see the iris in full bloom too. We call them the poor man's orchid: they always seem so neglected because they grow so plentiful I guess, right

29

in your own back yard. Our apricot trees have bloomed beautifully, despite the chilly winds of March. Now our peach blossoms are beginning to fill out. By Palm Sunday they should be bursting out like pink popcorn all over. I love the perfume of trees in bloom. No manufacturer can ever seem to duplicate its delicious sweetness—not even at fifty bucks an ounce! God has the only patent on the perfume He gives His trees." The letter ended with a verse which she had written.

After that was Margie's letter. She said: "The group letter arrived in this morning's mail. I have been looking forward to the letter for so many days, and all of your letters and all of you lived up to my highest expectations. You will all want to know a little about me. I was born January 3, 1923, in Philadelphia. I am the oldest of three children. My brother Francis is twenty-three and married to a sweet girl. Joe is twenty and one swell guy. I went eight years to Holy Child School and four years to Hollahan Catholic Girls High School. I worked for a short while at the Federal Reserve Bank and got married in April 1941. My marriage was very happy for awhile, but, as oft times happens, everything seemed to go wrong, and my husband and I separated in 1947.

"My marriage was not entirely in vain because I was blessed with two wonderful sons. Billy is eight years old and he is in the third grade. He gets along beautifully in school. This year he gets confirmed and makes his first Holy Communion. Joey is five, and he has just started to kindergarten. He loves it, which surprises me because he is a little stinker. My boys are being cared for by my mother and father, and I thank God every minute for granting me such wonderful parents. They love the children and the children love them

30

and are perfectly happy with them. My mother is doing such a beautiful job of raising them, God bless her.

"My tuberculosis was discovered in October 1949. I had been sick for quite awhile before that. The doctor who was treating me thought I had anemia. So as a result, I was a very sick girl when I went to a private sanatorium in Philadelphia. I stayed there for fifteen months, but it proved to be quite expensive. I was very fortunate to be able to come here to Deborah. It is only about thirty miles from my home, and I see my family every week. Deborah is a nonsectarian sanatorium, but it is primarily supported by Jewish Charities and workers. It is a beautiful sanatorium and I am very happy here, or at least as happy as I could be anywhere away from home. I have been taking pneumo peritoneum for three months. I hope and pray that this will help me at least to start on the road to recovery. I have had to stay pretty much in bed since I started my pneumo, but I keep myself pretty busy reading and writing letters. I did do some knitting but lost interest in it after awhile. My family bought me a seventeen-inch television set and it is truly a blessing. It helps pass the time, and it gives me and my cubicle mates many hours of enjoyment.

"I am so happy to be a part of your group, and I hope I will be able to be a good one. It has been such a pleasure to meet each of you, and next time I will know you a little bit better and I will be able to write each of you a message.

"May Glod bless and watch over each of you.
                    "Love,
                    "Margie."

And last of the initial letters was the letter from the chaplain, Father C. "The intention of our group is wonderful," he said— " 'That our soldiers in camp face temptation with

Christian courage.' Who thought of it? Our Patron Saint, Joan of Arc, couldn't have been better chosen. Am much interested in service people—I had orders to report to the chaplain school when my second heart attack forced me out. However, I have helped out in camps and have served close priest friends who are in service now. Am letting them know of our intention. Believe me, it is all right to brag and feel proud of the Mass attendance of our service people, but there are a few commandments to keep too!

"Whenever possible, I will offer Holy Mass for our group on the fourth of each month. (I have only one 'free' Mass a week for my own intention.) Of course, each Mass I offer, I remember our group at the memento, that you may all share in its infinite merits. (Unite with me each A.M.)

"The delay of the group letter on my part was caused by the fact that I have been helping out in parishes for four weeks and the last week my mail wasn't forwarded. Then too, the 'file' on me didn't arrive from Alcatraz—guess the warden was busy!

"Born November 16, 1900 (just a young lad!).

"1923—March 25—became a Catholic. (My background is Yankee and Puritan. I'm the only 'black' sheep.)

"1929—entered seminary in St. Louis.

"1936—ordained on August fifteenth in Des Moines, Iowa."

Then he wrote a list of the cities and states where he had lived and worked as a priest. They were scattered from Detroit to California and Louisville to St. Paul, and included a Negro mission in Birmingham.

"Most of my work has been retreat work for sisters, nurses, laymen and women, college and high school students. Have helped out in parishes and several large hospitals. My last work was preaching laymen's retreats at our retreat houses in Detroit and Cincinnati. Was sent here after my last heart attack.

"Which brings me to confessing I must be a member in 'bad standing' after reading the group letter, especially Jerry's. All that happened to me was a bad coronary thrombosis and seven attacks since, plus a couple of slipped discs in my spine—whatever a disc is. They will probably take me out back of the monastery when I am ninety-three and shoot me."

John Paul had to laugh at that with Miss Grey. This priest had a sense of humor. But he knew what suffering was. John Paul had once been on a ward with a man who had a coronary and had seen him with an attack. It wasn't pleasant. The picture was still in John Paul's mind of the man fighting and struggling for breath in the other bed until the doctors and nurses had rushed up to treat him, screening him at the same time from the view of the other patients.

But Father C. made light of it and joked about it at the expense of his brother priests. Take him out and shoot him indeed!

John Paul kept smiling when the laughter was gone as he motioned with his head for Miss Grey to go on.

"Thank God for a heaven—I keep saying we don't think enough of its *rewards*, and we priests don't preach enough about it. More later. Keep this 'faker' in your prayers and penance, and God bless all."

To begin the new round; this time Jerry had good news in his letter:

"All our prayers have been partly answered. During February I was making a novena to Our Lady of Lourdes, to find a way back. On the seventh day of that novena I got

33

wonderful news. A friend is going to send me back to Lourdes this summer. However, you must pray even harder for me, because I have to find a pilgrimage that will take sick people, and I also have to find a nurse to go with me. I also need strength in both body and spirit to go on such a pilgrimage. When I get to Lourdes again, I will remember you all in my prayers.

"Now, Claire, I will tell you about my dog. Between 1930 and 1933 I wasn't as helpless as I am now. I used to go out every day in my little hand car. I always took my dog with me. Her name was 'Puppy.' She really was only a mutt —half poodle and half spitz—but she was one of the best friends I ever had. We used to live in a neighborhood where the children used to treat cripples badly. One time before I got Puppy they turned me and my car over. However, it was a different story when Puppy went out with me. She used to walk right in front of me with her tail waving like a battle flag. She would never leave me. If she saw a boy or a group of boys coming near me she would stand still, bare her teeth and growl. Most of the time, they would run when they saw her doing this, but a few times they kept coming, and Puppy would jump and grab one of their coats. She wouldn't let go until they began to run, and then we would continue on our way. Puppy lived only three years, but during that time she had fifteen puppies of her own. She was run over in 1933. I never had another dog like her since.

"Every Easter except last Easter, I wrote an Easter letter to the Family. This Easter is almost the same to me as the Easter before I went to Lourdes the first time, so I think I will close this letter by copying the Easter letter I wrote then. Here it is:

34

"Happy Easter, everyone.

"This is the season of miracles. Firstly because it is Easter and Jesus performed the great miracle of rising from the dead. Secondly because it is spring, the time of the year when God performs a great but common miracle of making trees and flowers bloom again.

"Nearly two thousand years ago today Jesus rose from the dead by His own will. That was a miracle, but then His whole life was a series of miracles. He was born of a virgin. That was a miracle equal to His Easter one. However, He performed lesser miracles all through His life. He changed water into wine. That was a miracle, you and I couldn't do it. He made the dumb speak, the deaf hear, the blind see, the crippled walk and the dead rise. Those were all miracles, even our great doctors cannot do all these things. Jesus suffered and died and saved all the people from hell. He didn't just save the people that were living in His time. He saved all the people from the beginning to the end of the world. Although it looked like His greatest failure, it was His greatest miracle. No man could save every soul from the beginning to the end of time. Only Jesus could do this because He was God. A lot of people refused to believe these miracles because they think the Bible is just a fairy tale. I can see where they might doubt the Bible, because you do need faith to believe in it. But how they can live through a springtime and still say there is no God and no such thing as a miracle is beyond me.

"That kind of people say there is no God because they can't see Him. That is silly! They can't see the wind, but they know there is wind because they can see what it does. Yet when God makes the trees bloom and seeds grow into flowers, they still don't believe in God. They say it's just

35

nature. A man can make a thing that looks like a tree; he can make a thing that looks like a seed but he can't make it grow. A man can even make a thing that looks like another man, but he can't make it live. Only God can do these things. These are all miracles just like the ones Jesus performed. Yet those people say there are no such things as miracles. Those people also say they can live without God because they can't see Him. That is also very silly! They can't see air, but they could only live a few seconds without it. If they can't live without air, which is just another miracle of God's, they surely can't live without God.

"The reason why I am talking this way is, now that we are planning to go to Lourdes some people are trying to discourage me. Let me say this: the very fact that I get there will be a miracle, because I am not able to travel. If I am cured, it will be a double miracle, because I am not worthy to be cured. I will be very pleased and grateful if God lets me even see someone else cured. Now I wish you all a very happy Easter again."

John Paul was thoughtful when Miss Grey had finished this letter. She was silent awhile, and so was he.

"This Jerry must be some swell guy," he said at last. Miss Grey agreed.

Then she went on to Claire's letter. She too spoke of the wonders of spring.

"The weather has been beautiful of late. I awake some mornings around five and hear the birds chirping their hellos to the sleepy morning. Spring is my favorite time of year: God's handiwork seems so in evidence all around us. I have been very well of late. God has been so good to me because for so many years I knew only illness and weariness.

36

Since I have had Vicky and Michael too, things have been so wonderful for me. I am so grateful too.

"Recently I had a chance to go to New York to see 'La Boheme.' The only difficulty was, Vicky was not allowed to come with me. So I left her home for a day. I enjoyed the opera but missed her so much.

"I caught a noon train and just made the matinee, had dinner at the New Yorker and caught the 7 P.M. train back, felt lost without my girl to guide me. The opera was simply beautiful. I am buying the complete opera on records. Puccini's music is the finest, as far as I am concerned. . . . Now enough about my travels—it seems that my life is one big event after another; my little offering to God seems so little because the compensations He gives me make up doubly for my loss.

"I know what you mean by work, work, work. I try to schedule my work so I can rest in the afternoon. Vicky and I are learning our way around, and I even do most of my own shopping and buying. The subways are still beyond my courage, but some day I'll manage that too. John Paul, Lorenzo and Jerry, I am beginning a novena to Our Lady of Fatima for your needs. The book was put in Braille for me, along with the Novena to the Sacred Heart. I hope my poor prayers will help friends."

John Paul was especially pleased with her note to him:

"John Paul, I know what you mean by daily annoyances. It seems the little crosses are harder to carry than the large ones. I suppose we should think of these little hurts, sharp words and belittling deeds, as splinters from the cross. I too become quite vexed at little things, but I learned to push them aside. I used to make myself pretty miserable with unimportant things—mostly self-pity—but life is too wonderful and has too much to offer for us to pause only to com-

plain and feel sorry for ourselves. I don't even pretend to
be holy or give a sermon, but life passes quickly—little do
we know what tomorrow has in store for us. A priest friend
of mine who was killed in the Texas explosion last spring
told me to live each day as though it were my last and I'd
have a good life. I think that is a nice thought to tuck away
and call to mind when first awaking. I always try to say
my morning offering first thing, then try to keep in mind
that this may be my last day on earth. It does make a
difference. Oh, but be assured, I still get hurt, say things
I shouldn't, but at least trying is better than giving up."

Florence wrote:
"All the letters this round are so cheerful and happy I'm
beginning to think we're a pretty gay crowd despite our
aches, pains and worries. And how could I worry about
anything with the Little Flower taking over? What a
wonderful trip is in store for Jerry! I can picture him at the
great shrines in Lourdes, Lisieux, etc. And to think that he
will be praying for us! I visited Lourdes in 1939 and can
never forget what I saw there. I wish I might go back
some day.

"I left France on the last boat out of Le Havre, just as
war was declared. It was five o'clock in the afternoon as the
Normandie set sail. At six the war orders came in over the
radio—no lights that night—no more radio messages. The
Normandie was to zigzag on the Atlantic, going very far
north. Thrilling? I lay on my berth all ready for the worst
and didn't know another thing until morning! After the first
four days we got into American waters up near the North
Pole some place—it was so *cold*—and about the seventh
day reached New York. 'Twas a grand trip just the same.
Some time I'll tell you about the home of the Little Flower.

38

"We might discuss books and reading in our group letter, if you are interested," Florence suggested. "Quite a field for discussion here," she said. "I just finished the current *Catholic Digest* and the June *Extension*. In the latter is a remarkable article, 'Journey of a Jew.' It happens that I'm well acquainted with the author, his wife and little daughter. It is interesting the number of conversions from Judaism I have met in New York City, especially in connection with my work. But then, the Jewish population of New York is large—some two millions, they tell me.

"Now I have to leave you for awhile. In the meantime, I know you will remember me in your wonderful prayers. You will always be in mine. John Paul, you sounded a little lonely, but maybe some day God will make it possible for you to go somewhere too."

John Paul shook his head. "No," he said to Miss Grey as she read that part. "I used to dream about things like that when I was a child, but now I know better. It doesn't matter any more now though. I am content with what I have, learning to be. I am glad they can go. I can enjoy it through them."

Miss Grey smiled proudly at him as she lifted the book-letter again and started on Lorenzo's letter:

"I will be bedridden twenty years next month. Now don't all of you start feeling sorry for me, as I'm free of most of my pain now and my problem is to find ways of using up my time. Back in 1938 I was free of pain and I started a magazine agency and selling cards, as I told you last round. In 1942 I had my hips operated on, as my hips were locked as well as my spine and neck. I hoped to get motion into them and be able to sit on a chair and walk with crutches. God willed otherwise, as the day after the right hip was operated on, a clot went to the brain and my left side got paralyzed. It was a battle for a few weeks, and then six weeks later I had the other hip done, as I hoped the paralysis would wear off. But it didn't, so here I am. Lately I've been able to raise the head of my bed enough to write and with the help of a big clip to hold the paper. I hope you will overlook some of my mistakes.

"I have been reading the *Reader's Digest* condensed. I am about to start a book a friend let me take, *Murder in a Nunnery*. It's a murder that takes place in a convent. I hope you won't form too much of a bad opinion of me by my taste in reading, but that's how it happens to be.

"Father, I, for one, may have to call on you often for information, as I may be the black sheep of this group, who has never learned, or has forgotten, many of the important points of being a good Catholic."

"Not him but me," John Paul interrupted her reading to say. "Be sure and tell him that too in our answer. I never cared specially to know. Isn't that funny?"

"Stranger things happen," Miss Grey said and continued to read from Lorenzo's letter:

"All I can say is I'm trying all the time to improve, and with the fine company I'm now going to be in, I'm sure Blessed Martin will also lend a hand, he is my friend. So goodnight, and God bless you all.

"John Paul and Florence: I love to read, and I don't seem to tire of reading about others who have given so much for the Glory of God, and even though it may be fiction, it leaves you with a feeling of reality. I just finished reading the *Mass of Brother Michel*. I had read it five or six years ago. Next I'm going to read *Crown for Ashes* and *The Sign of Jonas*. Before I bore you on the subject of books, I'll change the subject.

"Miss Grey, we think you are wonderful to write for John Paul, and I nominate you as an honorary member of of our group. It was nice to see your picture, and I also think you are a pretty young Miss. I expect that you will be telling us about your boy friends one of these days, as those nice black eyes and dimples are very attractive. I'd like to say that, for a group, we take nice-looking pictures, and if only we could feel as good as the pictures seem to indicate, everything would be fine, except poor Jerry, who with so much suffering may not be able to hide it behind a picture. John Paul, I hope some time we will see one of yours."

He had enclosed one of his own too, and he was fine- and strong-looking, with a face full of character and patience. John Paul looked at the other pictures. Claire was young and pretty, with light hair framing a pretty face and Vicky standing beside her on guard. Florence was lovely as he had pictured her, with a face that suggested inner strength and peace. Margie Malley was little, with a delicate face set in a frame of bright hair. Father C. had a wide smile that invited confidence, on a very friendly face framed by hair on two sides of a bald spot that John Paul could see in the front. He looked like someone you could talk to easily. Lucille was also little and cute, with nothing about her suggesting long years of pain and helplessness. Her picture, like her letters, sang. John Paul was sorry too that he had no picture to send, but: "Just tell them I'm a thin scrawny guy with hair that sticks up and a long nose that sticks out—a real mug," he told Miss Grey.

But she wouldn't do it. "No, indeed I won't. First chance I get I'm going to bring my camera over, and we're going to take your picture so they can see for themselves what you are. And I like your nose. So there."

"You're the boss," John Paul said agreeably. "But only because I can't help myself."

"Just remember that," she teased him, rising to go. "I have to go now, John Paul, but we'll answer this tomorrow."

She left and John Paul was alone. It was good to be alone because he had something to think about, something to plan. He smiled to himself, planning his letter for the next day. Time passed thus so peacefully and happily that in a little while John Paul slept.

V.   Death Is a Door

That was a very peaceful evening for John Paul. George was off duty, and the new orderly was taking his place. He was very quiet and shy, but he knew his work and was quick and deft in his movements. He fed John Paul his supper, straightened his bed, and made him comfortable for the night. He didn't talk at all, except to inquire about his patient's needs and wish him a good night. "Good night, fellows," he said to all of them as he went out the door. "If you need anything, just ring or ask the next fellow to ring for you, if you can't."

John Paul fell right off to sleep, for a change—that was something that usually took him a while, especially when he had slept earlier in the evening, as he had today. He slept well and woke up the next morning very early, even before the orderlies had started bringing the basins of waters for early morning care. He lay there in his bed, thinking:

"God's love is a funny thing. He just loves us, and we can't see why He loves us even when we don't bother much about Him. Just waits, like He's got all the time in the world to wait for us to see He's worth bothering about—like He's got all the time in the world to wait for our love, and I guess He has though, at that. All the time in the world and beyond it. Just waiting and watching. Patient, not getting in a

43

hurry, taking His own time. Not jealous. What's He got to be jealous about in the things we love? . . . Nothing to Him, nothing. Foolishness. A child's tantrum. I used to throw a few fits myself. The nurses who worried about it suffered most from it and didn't help at all. The ones who didn't pay any attention, who didn't even seem to care, were the ones who cured me of them, and really I guess they cared for me the most too, because they wouldn't give in to the worst in me just for the peace of the moment, to shut me up. I guess God's like that.

"He made me crippled and useless, all but my soul. He left that free and strong, and now I can love Him or love myself. I can let myself be filled with self-pity or envy for others, or let myself offer my sufferings with His. Funny, that. And it's up to me. He won't force me. He calls me but I don't have to answer. Yet one day I am full of knowledge of Him and love of Him until nothing else matters but that. Yeah, funny. I couldn't describe it to anyone else, I won't quite remember all of it tomorrow—something will escape—that I can't catch again.

"But today I am so full of the joy of it that I want to sing and dance or shout for others to see, but since I can't do any of these things, all at once I know that this is also part of my joy, and it does not make me sad any more like it used to; instead I am content with it, with whatever He gives me. And considering everything, that's the funniest of all.

"On the cross He couldn't sing either, nor dance; and His only shouts were cries for help. He was thirsty, lonely, forsaken. He was a cripple then as surely as I am, and just as helpless then because He wanted to be. Yet that was His triumph as this can be mine. It is our Father's will, and our Father is God. It is through such things as this that His kingdom will come on earth as it is in heaven. This is the secret of Lorenzo's joy and Jerry's, so it must be mine. The suffering doesn't matter, but the joy of doing God's will. I am away behind them: yet I do believe I might catch up as I begin to understand. I do begin to see . . . just a glimpse . . . but I do begin to see. . . ."

An orderly interrupted his thought as he greeted him, bringing his tooth brush to brush his teeth. "Good morning, John Paul," he greeted him cheerily. "It's a nice day out; smells like spring. If you eat a good breakfast for me this morning, maybe I'll take you out for a little exercise after physiotherapy."

John Paul smiled. "Thanks, I would like that. I believe I do feel the ghost of an appetite too."

"Good. You don't eat enough to feed a dieting pigeon. How you keep going I don't know."

"Oh, there's not much of me," John Paul laughed.

"We'll have to do something about that," the orderly told him as he put a towel around his neck and began to wash his teeth, then his face. "We don't want you to blow away."

"That might be my only chance to fly," John Paul joked, as he submitted quietly to the ministrations. His day had begun.

When Miss Grey came in later in the morning after breakfast to write the letter for him, he was ready for her. He had already written his answer in his head and only had to dictate it to her:

"Dear Friends in Christ,

"Today it looks and smells like spring outside. I woke up happy and full of thoughts about God's love. I think it was your letter, Jerry, that did it, really. It is indeed a

45

miracle that God gives and renews life constantly for us when we are so ungrateful. Like you, Lucille, I find the letters from the group give me new hope and faith for the future because they always breathe joy, contentment, or at least resignation and trust in God's love. I don't think I had much of this before. I was always wishing I could die or asking God, Why? I think of all the things God hears, He must be tiredest of all of that one word 'why.' We always want to make Him accountable to us and we demand answers—then don't understand them when they come.

"Marge, you must understand this best, because in addition to the physical cross we all share you have a tremendous mental one too. We know it must be hard without your husband, plus being separated from your children too. But maybe you can take some comfort in the knowledge that if man's love is limited and changing, God's love is infinite and eternal, and your very cross shows that He has some special love for you. In His own time He will give you more—much more than He has taken, full measure, pressed down and running over. Miss Grey read me that in the Bible once. I like it. Makes God sound like a wonderful spendthrift spoiling His children just the right amount. I am saying it to you now because we all need at times the consolation of others telling us these truths which we find so hard at times to accept even though we know them. I will especially remember your little ones in my prayers; they must be fine boys.

"Father, I think you are a bit of a tease because you joke about your illness so, but I've seen a coronary attack and I know really it is not a joking matter, but a terrible thing, so you must have a lot of courage to be able to joke about it. I am glad you are able to offer Mass, and I am sure we all are grateful to you for remembering us in your Masses. I hope you will be with us a long time and think ninety-three is

N.B.

much too young an age for them to take you out and shoot you. Make it a hundred and ninety-three and I'll have Miss Grey wheel me over to the monastary and I'll shoot you myself.

"Jerry and Florence, what both of you say about Lourdes really fascinates me. As I told you, I have never been anywhere at all, not even around my own city that I remember anything about. I'd like to hear lots about your trips. It must be swell to be where the saints have lived and look on scenes that were dear to them. I sure hope you are able to go back again soon, Jerry, and you, too, Florence.

"Lorenzo, I can't say a thing about your taste in books except to wish they were fantasy instead of mystery so we could exchange books sometimes. I like C. S. Lewis and Merrit and Lovecraft. So maybe my taste is worse. At least you are in good company. G. K. Chesterton not only liked mysteries, he wrote many—the Father Brown stories.

"Claire, you amaze me: keeping house, going to plays, etc., with your handicap. Reading your letters, except for the parts about Vicky—who incidentally must be a wonderful dog—I would never guess that you were blind. Your Michael is a lucky guy, and you can tell him I said so. We will all be praying for your happiness together, and we hope too that some day our Lord will give him the grace of faith."

That was all. Miss Grey told him that she was proud of his letter and that made him happy.

After that the days were all different for him. He looked forward to receiving the group letters every six weeks or so; and more and more through his new friends he began to understand and appreciate the unique value of the offering he had to give to God, the value of suffering: and the mystery of it.

47

Miss Grey said that he was growing up in God. "We are all children of God," she told him one day, "but some of us remain children all our lives, spiritual morons, if you like, though I'm sure no one would want to be called that. God does not want that. He wants us to grow up spiritually, just as we do bodily, as any good father would. He wants us to be a credit to Him. We might say that all the saints—those we know and those we do not know—are God's men and women, even those who were physically children. To aim at sanctity in our lives is simply to aim at growing up. Heaven is not here nor there, but where God's love is. St. Catherine of Siena says, 'All the way to heaven is heaven, for He says, I am the Way.' "

As the months passed, John Paul found himself remembering parts of his new friends' messages long after he had sent the letters on. He found too that as his knowledge of them grew, so did his love for them and his concern for their worries and problems. He found it easy, too, to speak to them of his own self and problems, and knew that theirs was no second-class friendship, even though none of them had ever seen the other except by picture. Still their friendship was the real thing. They rejoiced with each other, and suffered with each other and prayed for each other together. When Florence was injured and had to go to the hospital, they felt as if it were a member of one of their own families. They were glad when she was able to be up again, even if it was in a wheel chair, but they were sorry again that this new injury would make her old job too difficult for her to continue. They prayed that she would get something else she liked as well.

They followed Claire's plans with interest and joy.
Once she wrote: "All your prayers for Michael surely

haven't gone in vain. We have both signed all our promises, and Michael doesn't have to go back for further instructions. We only were there twice. Father said Michael understood things, our religion, his duties and promises so well, that it wouldn't be necessary for him to keep coming back. Our dispensation has been gotten, the next step is our wedding. I have been making the Rosary Novena faithfully for Michael's conversion and that we can be married soon. I know the Blessed Mother will help us; she can't refuse when I mean it so much, and she must know how hard it is for me to say a Rosary. My mind is so easily distracted. Usually it is my girl who is the distraction. She hasn't learned yet that when I am on my knees I might be praying. She thinks I mean to play with her. So you see, I say my Rosary midst laps, wags and woofs and usually a paw on my shoulder. I try to explain to her, but I am afraid she doesn't understand. I actually pray for her, pray we will work well together and she will not find me too hard to live with."

John Paul liked that. It made him laugh. He liked all the letters for different reasons. He liked Jerry's and Lorenzo's because they were alike in their suffering and knew the same pains and trials he did. He liked Margie's for their courage, and Lucille's for their lightness and the little verse she added as postscript to all her letters.

Once she said:

> The flight of time has thrown
> the covers from the deep
> and lovely flowers leap
> from winter's heavy sleep.
>
> The wings of birds are flown
> from balmy southern skies

their warbling signifies
such timely lullabies.

The seeds of life are sown
with heavenly control
by heading for his goal
and growing with the soul.

It might not be great poetry, he thought to himself, but he liked it. He liked what it did for him. He liked her notes too, because they were always full of news about her mom and dad, aunts, brothers and sisters and their children. She especially loved one little nephew, Dale, and John Paul could almost see him growing and playing, full of life and mischief.

"Every time Dale gets scared of a bad thunderstorm he makes the sign of the cross. He says then he knows God will take care of him and make the storm go away," she said of him once.

John Paul found it easy to picture from her description her farm home with its rolling hills and trees, especially the elm tree by the back door where she liked to sit. He could imagine the ducks and geese who acted as watch-dogs, announcing the presence of strangers.

He liked Father C.'s letters for their humor and spirituality and Florence's because she had made of her handicap a ladder for others as well as herself to climb to better things, fuller lives. Often she was too busy to write more than a note, but when she did write he marveled at the things she accomplished and the spirit of them.

"You see," she told them once, "mine is called the 'invisible handicap,' so it is often hard to understand. Deafness is not appealing—it is trying to the patience of both the victim and those who must go out of their way to communicate with him. So it is often difficult to gain the co-operation of those whose help we need. Those who have adjusted well to the handicap are careful not to allow it to embarrass others if they can help it.

"Our handicaps teach us many fine lessons. They teach us sympathy (sympathy, not pity)—one of the 'marks of an educated man.' How clearly our dear first leader showed this the day I visited her, that restful understanding that puts a tense, handicapped person at ease.

"Thursday evening I teach my first all-Negro class in lipreading. That will be one of three evening classes. The other two will be made up of young people, fifteen- to twenty-year-olds and older people. Please, one small prayer from each of you for success. Especially pray for the work with the colored deaf. This is a new work and an experiment.

"Yes, John Paul, some of my clients are sad cases, and the saddest are the young people—yesterday for instance, a twenty-year-old girl losing her hearing and with it her friends, her social life and many needs and desires. We will do all we can for her. The old people too need help—losing their hearing, they are often shunted off into a corner and never included in family activities. The break their hearts from loneliness."

Father C. was the first to leave the group. His last letter always stood out in John Paul's memory because it was the last and because it came during a great trial in his own life. He had contracted a virus infection and was feeling low and depressed, as well as hurting in every muscle. Two social workers had paused outside his door and they were talking:

"It is really pathetic to see those poor wrecks of humanity inside," one had said soberly. "Sometimes it seems a crime to prolong their lives and their agony when death would be merciful. That young fellow on the end, in there, don't look now, but he's hopeless. He's been here all his life, crippled just like that. He never will be any good to himself or anybody else; he has nothing to live for, no friends, no family, never a visitor. But they keep feeding him, sticking tubes and needles and what-have-you into his wretched flesh, trying to keep life there when we all know, and he knows, that he would be better off dead. I know there are people who hold a different view, but I sometimes wonder if there is a God, if perhaps He won't hold us accountable for that, for the mercy we could have shown a suffering fellow creature by putting it out of its misery but we did not."

"Yes," the other had agreed with her, "we imagine we are so civilized, but really we are far from it. We are full of barbaric superstition and fear of death. Why, I had a case just the other day of a mother clinging to her idiot son. She wouldn't let me put him in an institution, insisted on keeping him herself, even though she has normal children who will grow up with him. They have a bit of money so she can do as she likes, but it is all so foolish."

John Paul was sick over it. He thought of the trouble he was to Miss Grey and was ashamed and full of something like despair. He knew, of course, that not all social workers, not even all in that institution, felt like that. But he could not think of that right now. All he could think of was: suppose they were right after all? He could not sleep and the pain was worse too. He mentioned these things in the group letter when it came the next day. He knew that he would never forget the things Father C. had said, because they kept him from despair.

"It is evident that deep down it is the spiritual devotion to Our Lord and His sacred sufferings that is the bond that holds our group so closely together. So keep up the good work for Him and the souls our prayers and sacrifices help. How easily your crosses can be changed from physical and mental ones to spiritual ones, the value of which we will never know until we appear in the Divine Presence. Never neglect that morning offering and renew that offering during the day if possible.

"None of this discouragement now, John Paul, that is the devil's pet walking stick, and he sure likes to conk us on the noggin, if he sees the chance. I do hope our prayers and penances will forestall any serious future troubles. Let us all get busy on this, then. But these are real crosses and we are only human, so keep on loving Our Lord and telling Him, 'You know best.' How wonderful heaven is going to be for us if we keep on being faithful."

Six weeks later, when the group letter came back to him again, he learned from Jerry that Father C. had died. That was not long after he had written in that group letter. The knowledge filled John Paul with awe.

Jerry had enclosed a letter from a brother priest who had been with Father C. when he died. He wrote: "He must have become suspicious when nothing was done any more for him except watch him, but he said nothing. In fact this was the most remarkable virtue he practiced during his whole time in the hospital and won for him the greatest esteem as being a very virtuous priest.

"In the afternoon his breathing became more a pant, the breaths short and fast. We recited the Rosary and had Father repeat ejaculations, which he did with real fervor. The end seemed not far off, and we recited the prayers for the dying. The chaplain had given him Viaticum that morning, and he had been anointed a second time a few days before.

"Once he turned to me and said, 'I just can't keep this up,' meaning his breathing. Sister Ann Lucy, the superior,

53

and Sister Therese Marie were there for the prayers and to the end, which came at seven-thirty and suddenly for all expectancy.

"He was conscious up to the very last breath. He suddenly stopped panting, as if in great pain, and raised himself by his hands. Sister said to me, 'I think he is having a coronary.' And Father answered, 'I am. This is it. I am going.' He pleaded to be let down and sister cranked the bed down. He clasped his hands behind my neck, I suppose to have something to hold on to. Then his hands dropped. A beautiful smile came over his face and that was it."

When Miss Grey had finished, they both said prayers for the dead for Father C. Then John Paul said, "I hope I have as much courage and faith as he did when my time comes. I often wonder, Miss Grey, whether, in the last count, it takes more courage to live well or to die well."

"It takes courage for both, John Paul, but I don't think it's your courage so much in death that is important as God's help, and your love for Him. If you have lived with Him in love, then I don't think you can die but with Him in peace. For those who love God, death is a door to those mansions Our Lord went to prepare for us. It is a door to His house, not your own, so you know you have no right to open it yourself, but must wait till He pleases to open it to you. Yet, once He does, one need not fear to go in. You just walk right in with joy, then, I'd imagine, as children in their father's house. You know then you have a right to be there, and it is your home forever."

"I guess you are right," John Paul told her.

"I believe so," she answered. "So it is living that is important for us as far as courage is concerned. It is while we live that we can act and choose. And only then."

John Paul smiled. "You have a wonderful faith, Miss Grey;

I hope a lot of it rubs off on me. Between you and CUSA you might make something of me yet."

"Oh, don't say that, my friend. I have very little to give you really, nothing of my own. It's all His grace. We just let it move us. I can explain those things, but I am a coward really, and weak, and not at all sure that I practice all these fine things I preach so well. So, you see, John, you must remember to pray for me too, and offer some of your sufferings as well. You know that you are doing God's will by simply being as you are and offering that to Him in love. You know because that is all you can offer Him. People like me sometimes are not so sure. Our temptations are different and our sufferings, but they are not less real for that reason. Don't admire me; pray for me."

Secretly John Paul admired her all the more for saying this, but charity kept him from saying so. He said instead, "I always pray for you, Miss Grey, every night and every day, and offer up my sufferings for you too, because you are my friend, and I just wish I had more to offer you."

She smiled and did a surprising but wonderful thing. She bent down and kissed him on his forehead. "I want no more than that, John; that is enough."

VI.   Hail Mary

After a few weeks had passed, John Paul received, like all the members of the group, a letter from Jerry telling them about their new chaplain, Father S., and asking their prayers for him. "He is a good chaplain," he said, "and we are fortunate to get him because he is already chaplain of another group."

Not long afterward, the group letter came again, and it included a letter from Father S., the new chaplain, himself.

"The letter just came to me the other day on my return from Omaha. I went there to consult an oculist in hope of saving whatever little vision there is left in my one good eye. There is not much hope, so we must smile and be resigned and say, 'Thy Will be done.'

"I would like to tell you about the joy of completing our new St. Joseph's Church and the fact that we have over four hundred people attending where none had gone to Mass on Sundays before. Now we have daily devotions, Rosary with explanation of the Mysteries and some thirty Holy Communions each day. It all seems a miracle due to the prayers of the CUSA. Even financially we can see the effects of the prayers of those in affliction. With only $15,000 we were able to put up an edifice that has been evaluated at $50,000, owing largely to the amount of donated labor and the fact that we were our own contractors. We mortgaged the building as soon as it was finished, and thus we were able to furnish it and put it at the service of our people. We put in the envelope system, and one can see the effort of our dear people, most of them so poor that they count every penny, making an effort to save enough to put ten cents, fifteen cents and even a quarter towards paying off the $15,000 we owe. All this is the effect of prayer, your prayers and sacrifices which I know are acceptable in the eyes of God.

"I had planned to tell you something about other countries where it has been my good fortune to be—British Honduras, Tyrol in Austria, Bogota in the republic of Colombia, South America—but this time I will tell you about a new little cross that in His divine goodness God has seen fit to send me, and then a few words about what I hope to do, so as to beg for your prayers that it may be carried out.

"Since Christmas my eyesight has become decidedly worse. I went to one of the very best doctors in the West, and after a very thorough examination and change of glasses, the verdict is 'nothing can be done.' It seems that with the very heaviest glasses I have but ten per cent vision, and without them there is only two per cent. This is not much for the amount of work undertaken and actually carried on. Most of the Mass I know by heart, and with a good preparation the night before, I can go through with the ordinary Masses. I am asking for the privilege of saying a votive Mass each day. My prayer is I may be able to continue saying Mass to the end. For a priest this is the most important thing in life. For this I ask your prayers.

"As for the future, there are two propositions which are awaiting the approval of our Rev. Fr. Provincial. I would like to carry on an apostolate of the confessional and spiritual direction. The ideal place for it is our church in St. Louis.

The last thirty years it has been my good fortune to hear over ten thousand confessions a year. If I devote myself to this exclusively and am at hand to hear at any time, the number may be doubled. Mere numbers, however, do not count.

"The second proposal is to be spiritual director for the Sisters and the nurses and the patients in one of our T.B. hospitals out west. The amount of good to be done is very considerable. Even without eyesight something can be done for souls.

"We need your prayers, however, and your sacrifices. I know God will hear you and will grant me the special favor of being able to say Mass every day and to do some good to souls even if we do it under special difficulties.

"Your letter I will have someone to read to me, and my share in writing can be done on the typewriter. The keys are nice and large, and there is no difficulty except in rereading what I have written. May God bless you all and prove to you by unmistakable proof that He loves you very dearly."

John Paul liked that letter. Again he wished to himself the same wish he had once voiced to Miss Grey while Father C. was chaplain of the group, that all hospital chaplains were Cusans, or at least had the practical understanding of human and spiritual realities that these priests seemed to have. He said it again aloud as Miss Grey prepared to go on to the other letters. Miss Grey nodded. "Yes, John Paul, and not only for hospitals but all over we must pray for wisdom and holiness for all our priests, that they may be real fathers to us and lead us in the paths God chooses for each of us with vision and courage." John Paul agreed, and she went on with the letters.

Jerry wrote: "Up to today there isn't much to report about my pilgrimage to Lourdes this summer. I have not been able to find one American pilgrimage going to Lourdes that will take sick people. In a way I think this is a shame, because I can't see much use in making a pilgrimage to a place like Lourdes without taking the sick with you. However, I will be able to join a pilgrimage from Belgium in August. I have not been able to find a nurse, so my father is going with me to take care of me.

"Thanks to God and Our Lady, I have never brought up any of my troubles in the group letter before, but I think I'd better tell you some things so you will pray for us as hard as you can.

"I am facing the most serious crisis of my whole life. There are many problems causing this crisis. When I went to Lourdes the last time I thought it would be nice to be helped by God and Our Lady, but I was content to continue living the way I always have if it was God's will. However, I am desperately in need of help from God and Our Lady because I don't see how I can continue this way of life. I am not so much in need of a complete cure but some change is needed badly.

"Here are a few problems causing the crisis.

"Problem number one is family misunderstanding. Someone I love very much misunderstands me completely. I am being accused of taking life easy and letting other people do all my work. I have even been accused of letting my body get into this terrible condition.

"Problem number two is that I am losing my secretary. She has been with me five and one half years. She took care of my mother during the last five months of her life. My speech is very bad, but she can understand what I say better than any person except my mother. My secretary

59

hopes to get a job helping a group of such cases as I am. So you can see what a problem that will be when I lose her.

"Problem number three is that my father is taking care of all my physical needs. But now he has heart trouble and he is getting old. When he can't take care of me any more, my sister won't be able to either, because she has babies to take care of.

"I have other problems too but I won't go into them. I didn't intend to start this letter this way, but two things happened that made me feel downhearted. The family problem took a sudden change for the worse, and then on top of that the doctor came to give me my medical certificate for the pilgrimage, and he said my case was hopeless. So that is why God and Our Lady have to help me some way. Please pray for me.

"In the first group letter I promised to tell you about my radio job. I'd better do it now, because this is the last chance I have to tell you about it. You see, I quit on March thirteenth, partly because I expect to go to Lourdes this summer and partly because the company I worked for didn't pay enough.

"The job would have been very good if it paid enough and had regular hours, but I used to have to work over twelve hours a day off and on, and I used to get only seven dollars a week. Most of the time I used to only work one week a month. Here is what I used to do. I checked commercials to see if they were broadcast on time, if they were broadcast at all and if there were any mistakes. I used to work in eleven-minute periods to see if there were any rival company commercials. I used to have to make out a report for each eleven-minute period. Sometimes I would have two of those periods in half an hour, then I would have to wait an hour or two before the next period. I got this job in December 1943 after writing to fifty companies.

"We are not far from the Easter season, so I will copy a little Easter story that I wrote for my family in 1945. I hope it will show the purpose for suffering more clearly. Here it is:

"There lived outside Jerusalem on the road to Calvary in the days when our Lord Jesus Christ walked the earth, a Hebrew merchant and his crippled son, Jesse. The son of the merchant couldn't walk. No, he couldn't even sit up. His father had to prop him up with cushions. Jesse was twenty years old, but because of the disease that afflicted him, his body was shrunk, so he looked much younger than he was. He suffered all the time but rarely complained.

"Being a good man, Jesse's father did everything he could to make him comfortable and happy. Every evening, after selling his wares in the market place, Jesse's father would come home and tell Jesse all that happened in the day. He would tell him about the people he saw and the stories he heard. Then he would read to him the Holy Scriptures. Yes, Jesse knew about God's promise to send His Son down to redeem the world and Jesse hoped that he might live to see God's promise come to pass.

"Jesse's mother was dead, and he would have been all alone every day while his father was in the market place if it was not for Anna. Anna was a young girl, the daughter of another merchant. She took care of him all day. She kept him amused by telling him the things she saw and heard in the city. So between his father and Anna, Jesse knew what was going on in the world around him.

"His father and Anna kept Jesse as comfortable and happy as they could, but there were long days and nights when the pain in his body became almost unbearable. He wondered, and then he remembered his Scriptures, and he knew that God put everything on earth for a purpose. Then he would

61

ask God to help him bear his pain even though he wasn't sure why God let him suffer.

"When the pain got worse Jesse would try to forget it by thinking how wonderful it would be if he lived to see God's promise come to pass. So, when Anna began to tell him the stories she heard about Jesus of Nazareth, the son of a carpenter, and His great miracles and His good works he began to wonder. Could it be, could it possibly be, that Jesus was the Son of God? Could it be possible that God's promise had come to pass? His father told him more about the great miracles which Jesus did, of the blind He made see and of the crippled He made walk. Jesus must be the Son of God.

"It was the morning after that first Palm Sunday that Anna came in and told Jesse that Jesus had come to Jerusalem the day before and of the great crowd that greeted Him. Jesse's hopes rose. Now maybe he could see Jesus himself, and he might be cured.

"Jesse's father was taken sick and there was no one to carry him to Jesus. Jesse was bitterly disappointed, but he knew it was God's will and he tried to bear it.

"That terrible first Good Friday came, and Jesse watched in horror from his window as they dragged the torn and bleeding Jesus along the road to Calvary. Jesse was in despair! This couldn't be the Son of God!

"Three hours the earth was silent and dark. Through that awful gloom Jesse saw in the distance the three crosses on that hill of death. As he watched the crosses the pain in his body grew worse, and he tried to think he might yet see God's promise come to pass.

"Jesse began to recall the Scriptures. He suddenly realized that the Scriptures said that the Son of God would suffer and die to save the world. Now Jesse realized the purpose of pain. It was to atone for the sins of the world. If you offered it up to God, you could help save a sinner and yourself.

Jesse looked toward Calvary, and somehow he knew Jesus was the Son of God. His pain was very great now, but he didn't mind it. He knew the purpose of pain and he offered it up to God.

"It was nearly the third hour after Jesus was crucified. Jesse lay in agony, but he was contented because he knew he was suffering with Jesus. He rested his head on his arm and he heard his heart beating very slowly. It sounded to him like the footsteps of his soul at the end of a very long journey. Suddenly the footsteps stopped, and he heard a sweet voice say, 'Because thou dost believe in Me, this day thou shalt be with Me in Paradise.' It was Jesus.

"After the great storm was over Anna went to see if Jesse was all right. He was dead, but on his face was a look of joy and peace. Jesse had seen God's promise come to pass."

Miss Grey ended the story with a trace of moisture in her eyes. They both knew that Jesse was Jerry and Anna and his father were Jerry's sister and father, and the knowledge humbled and shamed them both.

John Paul thought of his own frequent rebellion, and he knew that Jesse could have been himself too, but he wasn't patient enough, he wasn't brave enough, and perhaps he didn't love enough or have faith enough. He prayed for faith and charity, half aloud, and Miss Grey said "Amen." She knew that she needed those things too.

Afterward, she went on to Claire's letter. Claire was happy and bubbling over with it: "I am so sorry I have held up the letter for so long, and realizing all of you must be waiting and wondering. I'm mailing the letter even though I haven't heard it as yet. Perhaps after it makes the rounds our leader could mail it back to me and Michael can read over the letters.

"The group letter came the day before our wedding, and

you can imagine the excitement and confusion around our home. The Blessed Mother gave us a beautiful day with sunshine and warm air. I shall never forget the beauty of that precious day and the warmth and good wishes that surrounded us and the peace that flowed into our hearts. When the snapshots come I'll enclose them for all to see.

"Thank you all for your good prayers and affectionate good wishes.

"We had a wonderful stay in Washington, then rented a car and drove to parts of Virginia. We saw the old town of Williamsburg that dates back to the late 1690's and walked down the old streets. We saw the hitching posts, old English-style fences, etc. I shall never forget our wonderful days of adventure. Went to Mass in a small church in Fredericksburg, Va. Vicky wasn't her good self in church, but the priest just smiled at her when she stood up on the seat and looked around. I went to Communion and felt so at peace, and perhaps, even closer to our dear Lord.

"Michael kneels beside me at night and we say our night prayers together. I am sure he will be one of us, some day.

"We are settled in our lovely little home in Jackson Heights. The housework keeps me busy and cooking keeps me busy too. In fact, I have been rather worn out these past few days, as my mother spoiled me, and rising so early and working all day has caught up with me. But Michael is the dearest and kindest husband and helps me in so many ways.

"We have so much more work to do here before our house is completely in order. I wish all of you could visit me here. I am just so proud of our home.

"I must cut this short, as it is nearly 10 P.M. and Vicky must be taken out, the kitchen has to be scrubbed (Michael is doing it, but I want to help) and the table has to be set for breakfast.

64

"Forgive me, dear friends, and many, many thanks for your prayers."

Florence had only a very short note, for she was very busy at her new job, but she promised more later, and wished Claire happiness.

Lorenzo wrote: "You really gave us a nice long letter, Father. This time also it does us good to hear you tell us that even in our helpless way we are doing something worthwhile. Last month a good friend of mine died who had been bedridden for seventeen years. Bob and I would talk over the phone for hours at a time. I'm sure he has a nice place, and so many of our questions have now been answered to him. Maybe he has found out why the Red Sox can't win—or doesn't God bother with such trivial matters.

"Claire, we hope you will be very happy and we are sure you will. May God bless your marriage."

John Paul and Miss Grey laughed a little at his question, but they were not laughing at him. "We'll have to remember to tell him that nothing is trivial with God," Miss Grey said.

"And," John Paul added, "I doubt very much that it is trivial to the Red Sox themselves. No, I guess God is concerned with even such things as this. And I hope his team does win this year."

They went back to the letter again. Marge wrote: "The group letter arrived yesterday afternoon, and as always I was so happy to receive it. I have read it over and over again, and honestly it's amazing how close I feel to each of you.

"I was deeply impressed at how powerful our little group must be at storming heaven. Imagine getting an answer to our prayers for a chaplain so quickly, and such a nice chaplain too! I already feel as though I know you, Father, and I am looking forward to your letters.

"I spend most of my time reading. My friends keep me well supplied with magazines, and I read quite a few novels. Speaking of novels—I guess you have all read *The Cardinal*; it's excellent reading.

"I also enjoy listening to the few really good music programs that are on the radio. I am learning to appreciate the classical music I wouldn't even listen to before I got sick. Now I realize how beautiful a symphonic piece can be and how an operatic aria can stir the emotions. There is so much beautiful music, and indeed we can thank God for it.

"Anyone reading this besides us would think: Boy! Is that the life? Nothing to do but lie in bed and read and listen to music. But we all know how boring it can get after a while, and that is when I turn to prayer.

"My boys are fine, thank God. They write me the sweetest letters. Billy tells me how he is teaching Joey to spell because he wants Joey to be the smartest boy in the room when he goes to school. He's quite proud of his little brother. Joey is another Jerry Lewis for sure. When I speak to him on the phone he tells me so many jokes and riddles, I don't know where he gets them. He's really a riot.

"I want to ask each of you to say a special prayer for my cubicle mate. She is thinking seriously of becoming a Catholic and I would love to see her become one. She is such a sweet girl and has suffered so much. I know how happy being a Catholic would make her."

Lucille was cheerful as always, but she had bad news this time. "It is very warm here in dear old Missouri today. Mom is typing for me this time. You see, I cracked my ribs again, this time on the right side. So I'm all taped up, and that means I have to be quiet for a while. Last time it took eight weeks to mend. I have five more weeks to go. I'm itching to get back with my typing, but if I do too much moving around it will take longer to heal up. But with the assistance of God and my dear mom—why, I'll come through okay. Lorenzo's baseball is our hobby now, we are pulling for the Cardinals—also the Browns.

"Tonight we will keep the Holy Hour. Cozyhill is wonderful to us. We have rivers and lakes nearby. Dad took Dale out to fish on Decoration Day, and they caught a few. Little Dale was tickled because he could bring some fish home.

"Decoration Day was my folks' forty-first wedding anniversary—also the second for my kid brother and his wife, Russ and Viola. We did not have a big celebration, just a chicken supper for the family. It was quite homey and pleasant.

"This will be rather short this time, so please pardon me as this gal brings this little note to a halt."

Enclosed was a poem, "My Days with You," dedicated "To My Mom":

> To see the day awake
> fills my heart anew
> with tender dreams again
> of days I shared with you.
> That day in early morn
> I found your sunlit hair
> so bright with golden lights
> that seemed like Heaven's prayer.
> And then the day began.
> The passing hour reflects
> your shining smile of love
> I know my heart expects.
> I learned to live with joy

Despite a hurt that grew,
I took it all because
my days were spent with you.

"She must love her mom a good deal," Miss Grey remarked as she finished. "She is always so full of praise for her."

"Yes," John Paul said, sighing a little. "I wish I had a mom like her, or father and sister like Jerry. Everyone seems to have someone but me. I've always wondered, do you know, thinking about how I came here, did my mom love me? Is that why she ran away and left me, so someone else could give me the care she couldn't, or was it she just didn't care?"

John Paul turned an agonized, pleading face to Miss Grey, and she almost turned away from the pain, but she made herself face it. She placed one hand on his forehead and impulsively bent to kiss him. "She must have cared, John Paul, I am sure of it, for anyone would love such a boy. Perhaps she was poor and could not care for a little baby like you, so she brought you to a place where she knew you would receive the care you needed which she could not give. But even if, by some unimaginable circumstance, she did not, what does it matter now? The only One in the whole universe whose love really counts loves you, and He has proved it. Whatever her intentions were in bringing you to an institution like this, He has made them right long since. He has seen that you have food and care for body and soul, and given you others to love you, little unimportant others, like myself, but doesn't our love count?"

John Paul lifted his head to kiss with reverence the hand that had rested on his forehead. "Of course it does, and besides that, you have taught me to know and love that other Mother, that God Himself gave us. May He and she give you the peace you give others, and the same happiness."

VII.   Growing Up

The weeks passed and the months and a year. John Paul was happy even when they moved him to another ward and he knew his condition was growing worse. They did not tell him. They did not have to tell him, he knew. He knew because the others in the new ward were sick and because they took his temperature more often now and gave him medications he had never had before. He knew because it seemed at times his body was one big ache. His hips were sore from the injections he was receiving. He asked Miss Grey one day what they were for.

"It's some infection, John Paul, and it is pretty deep. Probably from one of the bed sores. They're trying to fight it with penicillin and streptomycin. But don't worry about it."

"I'm not worried about it now, I know this has to end and there's heaven. The rest doesn't matter. I'm not afraid of the pain any more, even when I keep wishing it would end. I just think about heaven. This is the way Our Lord walked. I'm hoping He'll give me courage all the time, so I won't be afraid to walk it with Him."

"Yes, it is the way, John Paul. It is at times a hard way and full of dangers; yet He says, 'I am the way.' I can't understand it and you can't and nobody else can, not even the wisest or smartest, but we believe it's true because He said it. It's a queer way for our thought and logic and understanding, a strange way that we can't help fearing a bit at first, but love makes it easy."

"Yes," John Paul agreed with an odd smile on his face that held not only joy but something like triumph too, and something like surrender. "Love makes it easy."

Many things happened during those months. For one thing, John Paul became in turn a liaison officer, then a group leader in CUSA.

He felt a bit queer, almost lightheaded at first, when he became head of a little family, but he took the responsibility, not himself, seriously, and soon found it easy to carry out his new duties. He smiled at Miss Grey reminiscently the first time he found himself explaining some of the inner realities of CUSA, remembering that day when Miss Grey had introduced him to the group. Then he had understood nothing. Now he was explaining it to others. Once he had Miss Grey write for him to his little family: "We must try to be faithful too to our prayers and offerings of our sufferings as Cusans. There is so much we can do if we will. There is our holy hour, for instance. Some CUSA members have chosen a different hour for their part in nocturnal adoration, but most of us pray from 9 to 10 P.M. The hour is not the most important, the important thing is that we pray together as a family, for we are a family in Christ, remembering that 'The family that prays together, stays together.' Our Lord says: 'Where there are two together in My Name I am in their midst.' So you can see how close He must be to all of us when the whole of CUSA besieges heaven in His name.

"We can take much consolation in this holy hour if we realize that by it we are trying to respond to that plea Our

Lord uttered two thousand years ago in the loneliness of His passion: 'Could you not watch one hour with Me?' We want by this hour to bridge those years so we may suffer with Him for others, and for our own selves, that we may be made like Him."

Another time, when he was writing to his "little family" after someone had said what a good leader he was, and especially what a wonderful head they all had in their foundress, he said: "Don't give me any credit for being a good leader; I didn't know anything but the abc's of our faith until I came into CUSA, and whatever I know now has been learned through this. I'm just a copy-cat, borrowing the good I find here and passing it on. As for our foundress, of course we all love her, but she says the real foundress of our American CUSA is St. Catherine Labouré, so I think we should all try to practice a special devotion to her. You see, our dear leader had been praying and searching with no success at all for a way to start a branch here in America of the International Catholic Union of the Sick for a year and a half. Finally she asked the new saint, Catherine Labouré, on the day of her canonization, to make this possible. On that very day, she spoke to the priest who became our first chaplain, and after a moment of thought and prayer, he agreed to be the first chaplain and to help her. So they both say St. Catherine is our real foundress. So, you see, we have much to be grateful for, much for which we can give thanks. And speaking of thanksgiving, you all will be happy to know that the students of Notre Dame have been praying for and with us for a minute after Mass and Communion and in their visits to the Blessed Sacrament, especially as thanks to the new group in CUSA, who have for their intention 'the success of Holy Cross Congregation in all its apostolates all over the world,' and for their motto

'The Cross Our Only Hope'—which is the motto of the Congregation. I'm sure all of us are grateful to them for remembering us, just as much as they are to this group for remembering them. The charity and goodness of God unites us all and spills over in joy and good things as well as suffering. We are one in Christ. How often must we remember that and ponder it."

He loved his new groups, especially the one where he was leader. He had thought once that he could never love another group like the first one, but he quickly found out how wrong he was, especially as he watched the members of his own infant group grow in love of each other and of God in the finest Cusan spirit. He felt a certain good pride that gave God both the credit and thanks as he watched the members in his own group grow in God-consciousness and social-mindedness.

He found himself looking forward to the CUSA bulletin too, for the helps it gave him, and especially so after Harry, the "Roving Reporter" whose roving was confined mostly to his own bed, started his column, for the humor too and the news about other groups.

Harry became known as the Mascot, and he jokingly began calling their general leader "Mother Abbess," a nickname first given her by their first chaplain.

He liked Harry because his sense of humor hid a depth of thought in spirit—no, it didn't really hide it; rather it revealed it in a way that compelled yet gave no offense, convinced yet didn't frighten. He wondered how Harry had come into CUSA and was very pleased to read Harry's own account of it later in a Christmas newsletter. It was a quotation from a letter which Harry had originally written to his brother, a Benedictine monk:

72

"Until three years ago, you know that Christmas was a drear, dark day for me. Even the holiness of the time could not make it brighter or happier. Nearly always alone and knowing that if I were not the mess I am, physically, I need not be alone but rather a part of a large and happy family group. The season was desolate with the knowledge that any gifts which might come my way would be sent out of a sense of duty, or what is worse . . . pity. I felt alone in a world of healthy, happy people. People who were not an awful expense to those who loved them. People who could go out into the holiday crowds and make merry. And I could sit at home. If I could sit. Half the time not even able to get to Mass.

"And then one day, a letter came to me, one I didn't pay too much attention to at the time: would I please read the enclosed folders? Naturally, bein' the polite chap I am, I read them. They told me about the Catholic Union of the Sick in America. Rather an imposing title, isn't it? And rather an imposing organization it is, too. You know what folly it is for anyone to ask me to write a letter; that I will write a letter at the drop of a hat and that mostly no fallen headgear is needed to get me into a letter-writing mood, and when the folders asked me to write a letter, write a letter I did. That was the beginning. Within a few weeks I began to find letters in my mailbox—letters from all over the country—letters from people handicapped in every imaginable way. A lovely girl who is working hard to combat T.B. and a bad heart. Beautiful physically and radiant spiritually. That was number one. And then a friend of hers . . . another sweet girl, tall and slender and as full of mischief as she can be. Lest you suspect me of being partial to pretty girls, there is the young man of my own age or close to it, a saintly young bird who will probably spend his purgatory making puns, the ones he makes now are so atrocious. And then a truly beautiful spirit, an old lady who has since gone to heaven. That was our Grandmère who wanted to lead us 'to Jesus through Mary.'

"I was feeling so very happy to be making friends, a thing I had not had the chance to do before. And another letter came. This time it was from the foundress of the American CUSA. She wondered if I didn't think it would be a good idea to start pulling on the oars a bit rather than just drifting along for the ride. How about doing some work? Now I assure you, she didn't say it just that way, but I got the idea. Can you imagine how that made me feel? Here was a wonderfully sensible woman . . . with brains, no less, asking me if I'd like to do something? Here I've been going along with the current notion that I was not quite bright and that it was only by the grace of God I knew my left hand from my right! I jumped at the idea. And I found myself doing something for someone else.

"Just about that time it was Christmas, and with Christmas came what I have learned to call a small CUSA miracle. I wish I had a real skill with words to really describe a CUSA Christmas. It is like nothing you could ever dream possible. The member, no matter how lonely or depressed, finds himself inside a warm and glowing family circle with no one left outside or neglected. It is as though someone had constructed an Advent wreath and used the broken and twisted limbs as branches and evergreen. Evergreen with Faith. Fever-bright eyes and cheeks as hollyberries and the burning flame of pain as the candles. As each day draws one closer to the Great Day, the prayers and thoughts of others, the sweet knowledge of being remembered, add flames of joy to the wreath, until on Christmas Eve the whole radiant Advent wreath is blazing with love and the sense of be-

74

longing. Each member is bound by love and loyalty and the strong knowledge that each is using his cross of pain to best advantage . . . or if not yet . . . is striving to do so. The CUSA family realizes that it is a vast potential and is trying to use that valuable pain-potential where it will do the utmost for souls.

"On a very ordinary plane, what fun it is to belong to CUSA at Christmas time! The prospect of mail each day, wonderful, brightly decorated mail. Simple cards, elaborate ones. The veddy, veddy formal ones. The ones lovingly fashioned by hands because the sender likes to be original and likes to include a bit of herself with her holiday mail. A couple of extra handkerchiefs for a nose sadly afflicted in the winter by colds and in the summer by hay fever. A very fancy bit of neckwear which clashes horribly with red hair. (No hurt feelings here; no one has given me a tie!) A book . . . or after a lot of wailing for one certain book . . . three or four copies of the same one. Or perhaps a grand pipe in a swank case, far too grand to fill with smelly tobacco when you learn that the case is a pouch. And the wonderful, oh-so-lovely Christmas letters. The dear grand women who realize that an all-male household isn't very gay and so try to supply the woman touch. The tips on how to fix a holiday meal the way New Englanders do . . . or how to cook a turkey after the fashion of a proper Detroiter. And the best advice of all comes from out Minnesota way, from one of the authors of the family who tells you how to *eat* the dinner after the Irish fashion. And the news of Christmas in a children's nursery from the real-live book author who cares for a lot of little ones who otherwise could be neglected.

"But the jewels of the Holy Day mail are letters from the chaplains with the promises of a memento in Midnight

75

Masses. The precious bits of prayers and ejaculations from all the friends and loved ones of the family. Christmas in CUSA is a happy time.

"But it isn't always Christmas and the mails aren't always full of holiday brightness. Sometimes the days are dull and gloomy and long, and then a letter comes; a letter full of heartache, and a chap is forced to snap out of his own fit of depression to send a letter of encouragement and love and promises of prayers, and after the letter is written, the load is lifted from at least one pair of shoulders . . . and if it was well written . . . from two! That is one of the most valuable fruits of CUSA . . . the joy of knowing that no heart is too lowly nor pocket too empty to be able to lend the help of an understanding heart and the powerful weapon of prayer. A chap learns that he isn't here on earth to coddle his aches and pains and nurse his hurt feelings, but he's here to use them for his own soul and the souls of others. The only thing is . . . a very weird thing happens! When the pains and hurts have been offered up, there doesn't seem to be anything else left to offer! Now there is a silly statement if ever there was one! (And I'm noted for my silly statements.) What is wrong with offering up joys and little happy endings and the nice things of day-to-day living? Warm shaving-water for a change. Good hot coffee and dark chocolate cake. Fresh, crisp sheets, smelling sweet and fragrant from the line. Being able to see something of your visitors besides feet—but then, if a fellow were truly charitable, he'd consider the comfort of the visitor. Perhaps the back of my head is much more appealing to the eye than my face! But there are so very many things to be thanking God for. Even curious brothers who ask questions and thus give me a chance to talk for pages and pages. Have I answered your questions properly? About what has been happening to me lately? CUSA has been happening to me . . . and it is swell."

Besides this, John Paul especially liked to read the quotations from Marguerite Marie Teilhard which frequently appeared in the bulletin. She had been president of the French Union of the sick until her death in 1936, and although advised at one time to give up the presidency of this union because of her great suffering she had replied, "Leave my sick people? Never! It would be abandoning the crucified Christ!" She wrote with wisdom and humor, and often John Paul wished he could get people like George, the orderly who had been such a trial to him on the other ward, to read what she said. People who thought talking about suffering was morbid. "How efficacious the prayer of the sick must be to keep the devil so busy by putting obstacles in its way," she had said once.

John Paul smiled, a little self-conscious, half-guilty smile, at that, because it hit home. He was having a hard time praying lately. At first when he had begun to understand something of the reality of God's being and love, he had been full of joy, and the joy had spilled over spontaneously into prayers of love, praise and thanksgiving. He made the offer of himself every morning, and his suffering, with a sort of exultation and impetuous generosity of fervor. Nothing had seemed hard or impossible to suffer and offer, and he had spent hours, in days that had heretofore been long, empty and meaningless, in spontaneous meditation on the goodness, glory, power, and love of God; and time had passed so quickly he had been unaware of its passing. He had delighted in reading books about God and the saints and couldn't seem to get enough of authors like Thomas Merton and Father Leen, two of Miss Grey's favorites whom she

77

read to him often or let him read. They had fixed up a way for him to read by turning the pages of a book himself with a little gadget he held in his mouth. Learning to use it had been awkward and difficult at first, but now he had mastered it quite well, and could read alone easily if someone else would just prop the book up before him on the stand. He had read the *Imitation of Christ* and the Gospels with a spiritual greediness that would not be sated.

Then, gradually, all this had changed. He found less and less delight in reading and prayer and more and more reasonable excuses for not doing either—the orderlies were too busy, he ought not bother them to fix the book; he needed something light and humorous for relaxation; he couldn't concentrate on prayer just now, maybe later when it was quieter in the ward. Meditation became a difficult trial to his patience and test to his faith. He could not picture any scene from Our Lord's life nor any saint's life, and the more he tried to concentrate on the inner meaning of their words, the less he understood them and the more his mind wandered. It was as if his whole soul had suddenly been plunged into an unfamiliar darkness and wandered there afraid, going deeper and deeper into the blackness the more it struggled to find brightness and relief. At times it was almost as if God were not—as if John Paul had been plunged into an eternity of emptiness.

Yet, paradoxically, there was something else too, a thread, a faint path in the darkness, not of light, but almost of a deeper darkness; yet somehow, in a way he could not understand, express or explain, comforting. That was not always so, but the memory or half-consciousness of it was always there, and when he made himself spend his accustomed time in trying to read or pray, even though he did not feel that he was praying or understanding what he was reading. This half-conscious knowledge of what he did not know, and understanding of what he did not understand, filled him, way down beneath the doubts, fears and uncertainties of the darkness, with a kind of certainty that somehow all was well, or all was going to be well. And at those times he knew something that was a little like peace, but not peace exactly, a little like joy, but not joy either, as he had understood it in the past; something that had no name, that could not be described or expressed, that was neither felt nor known as he understood feeling and knowing, yet somehow it was there.

Sometimes this thing filled him with exultation and happiness so that his spirit sang and he knew nothing in the world mattered like that. He knew he had received that priceless gift from God that was the treasure hidden in the field which the man who found it sold all his goods to possess.

Most of the time it was weariness and monotony in trying to pray without feeling or words, and wondering if after all one was not wasting time. Most of the time it was fighting an insidious voice inside which insisted he wasn't praying at all, he was a hypocrite, spending all that time pretending to think about God when really his mind was attending to other things, complaining of pain, resenting helplessness, day-dreaming and musing. Sometimes there came upon him the feeling that he couldn't pray because he was not worthy to pray, the feeling that God had no use for him and his worthless prayers after so many years of neglect and sin against graces given and refused. He had neglected God all these many years, not loving Him, not caring about pleasing Him: why should God bother about him now?

As best he could, he fought against these insidious suggestions of the tempter in his own mind, and in agony of spirit cried silently to God again and again: "Lord, I believe, have pity on my unbelief. Teach me to pray. Teach me to love You. I want so much to pray. I want so much to love You. Pity me, Lord; You are a God of mercy. Show me Your mercy, lest I leave You from my own weakness. Teach me to love. Teach me to pray. Have mercy on me."

He could not bring himself to write all this in the group letter, but he did write some of it, enough for the others to understand, especially if they had already gone through the same thing. And it pleased him to find in the bulletin someone who had written of some of the same problems. No, the devil didn't spare any effort in putting obstacles in the way of the prayer of those determined to serve God more perfectly.

Another time in the bulletin Miss Teilhard wrote about perseverance, and once more John Paul found himself in her story about "Coralie." The heroine of her story had gone through the exact exultations, consolations, difficulties and finally distresses that John Paul had experienced from the first days of his membership in CUSA till now. She was saying to a priest what John Paul often said to Miss Grey in his desolation:

"It would be enough for me just to have God's help alone, but even that is lacking now."

"God is never lacking," the priest told Coralie (and John Paul knew that the same might have been said to him). "It is you who are lacking in generosity."

"Haven't I given Him enough of that?" she replied. And as he read this, John Paul's face flamed in shame, because he knew himself guilty of just such feelings and words.

"Yes, but now you are trying your best to take back as much as possible of your gift. The more you give to Mother Nature, the more demanding she becomes; and the discomfort caused by your resistance to divine grace is perhaps the source of your impatience and distress. My child, in your situation, you must choose between saintliness or just plain mediocrity. Once the Passion begins, any intermediate position is impossible. At such a time Our Lord does not condone sleeping or stopping to warm oneself. Nevertheless, in the Garden of Olives, sleep was the downfall of the best apostles, and St. Peter himself fell by the way to Calvary because of the warmth of a fire. Except for St. John, they all nearly lost their souls because they were so fond of their little comforts. You will suffer much less by being more faithful. Watch and pray."

Yes, John Paul decided, Marguerite Teilhard knew about people like him. She understood. Yet neither did she go overboard about suffering or sacrifices. On the contrary; once, in answer to a person who had complained, after being miraculously cured of illness in answer to prayer, "I have come to the conclusion that I have missed my vocation," she said: "What vocation, Seraphine?"

"That of suffering."

"There is only one true vocation: the vocation to the will of God. Our Lord worked until His thirtieth year. He devoted three years to His public life and allowed suffering to render Him helpless in the eyes of men for the space of twenty-four hours. Do not conclude from the Gospel, therefore, that perfection comes from asking for illness. Christ healed the sick and wept over them. Suffering was a very ugly thing when it came into the world as a consequence of sin. Christ transformed it for our good, but He blessed it only because of the compensations it would gain for us. In fact, it acquires beauty only when we begin to struggle against it. The sick person who neglects the means of recovery, in misguided devotion, is on the wrong track. His duty is to fight to regain health, and that very struggle leads him to the vocation of suffering.

"It is illusion to look for it in any other direction . . . and as for amateur Victims, be careful about them. If a member of the spiritual aristocracy remains nevertheless difficult to live with, disobedient to doctors' orders, neither lovable nor loved, sensitive, incapable of occupying himself usefully even when he could do some work, I would have grave doubts about his vocation. Let's not get tired of cultivating the everyday virtues before we aim at the extraordinary ones, and remember that the love of God, far more than suffering, creates victims."

John Paul remembered that too. It was his answer to George and to all the others who misunderstood. It wasn't the suffering that mattered, it was the will of God that delighted. One rejoiced to suffer for love's sake; only, it was the love that mattered. One suffered gladly because in it one found the will of the Beloved, of God, and one embraced His will with joy because it pleased Him to show Himself this way. Nevertheless, sometimes in the darkness of one's night, one prayed to the Beloved to have pity on one's weakness, and it was not wholly in fear that one prayed so, but in response to grace too. John Paul had learned that. And always it was the love and surrender that mattered. One would have surrendered as easily to a different appearance, a different vocation, if God had called one so. So this vocation of suffering, like any other, is not, must not be, one's own choosing, but the loving response to a call of God. "You have not chosen Me," He had said, "but I have chosen you." How well John began to understand it.

N.B.

All the important things that happened that year in the group were not concerned with John Paul, though of course all meant much to him.

Jerry came back from Lourdes again uncured but with the same undaunted spirit. "Among other consolations for not being cured," he said in his first letter after he came back, "one of the greatest is that I still belong to CUSA. No—I wasn't cured. In fact, I came back exactly the same. I still have all the problems to face that I told you about before I left—but somehow they don't seem as big as they did. Our Lady has given me new strength and courage to face these problems—and what is more important, she has given me peace of mind. I didn't want to go back to Lourdes just to be cured. I wanted to go back to make up for some of the wrong things I did the first time I was there. I feel now that I have made them up, and that although to the outside world my trip looks like another failure, it was really a great success to me.

"A long time ago when I was a little boy I used to think it was God's Holy Will that I was a cripple. Now, after two visits to Lourdes, I am pretty sure that God wants me to be a cripple for the rest of my life. This does not mean I have any feeling of hopelessness or self-pity. It is just that I have come to feel that this is my 'Vocation.'

"In these terrible times we are living in, I think God needs every crippled and sick person who is willing to try to make up for all the sins of the world insofar as is able."

Claire had the best news. One month she wrote: "We have been house-hunting too, and we beg your good prayers for this intention. Coupled with that, the biggest of all, we are expecting our first baby in mid-November and we are so happy about it. I ask your daily prayers that all will go well for my baby and me. I haven't been too well and have lost weight instead of gaining, but the doctor isn't alarmed. I am starting to feel better now, but it had been hard these past few months. Just so everything turns out all right, I won't mind the discomfort at all. Can I count on your Aves? I am sure I can."

Then there was good news from Florence. After she was injured in the accident she had been for a long time in the wheel chair, but now she walked with the help of a cane. The job she had been doing became too much for her, but she had decided to take a job teaching in a southern college.

She said "My locomotion leaves something to be desired, but at least I get around and I can hope for constant improvement.

"I think I'll tuck in a little smile here: It seems that sister asked the children to contribute to the pastor's spiritual bouquet, marking the anniversary of his ordination. One little boy put down: '200 litanies to be said during recess.'

" 'But Tommy,' Sister said, 'You can't possibly say two hundred litanies in fifteen minutes.' 'Oh yes I can, Sister. I just turn to the place in the prayerbook and say, "All the saints on this page, pray for us!" Then on the next page, "All the saints on this page, we beseech thee hear us!" Then on the third page, "From all the things on this page, O Lord, deliver us!" '

"Now I'll say goodbye for this time. I'll be praying for you all."

Lucille told them she was sick again. "Mom said I get too frisky. I want to do so much but I can only do so little. The spirit is willing but not the flesh."

Marge had a day at home with her children for the first time in seventeen months, and her happiness spilled out all over the paper. Billy was confirmed and made his first Communion, and she sent pictures of him looking very angelic, also one of Joey.

Father S. had the operation on his eyes and it was successful, enabling him to see not perfectly but enough to do his work. But he had to give up his church and was assigned instead to a college in the west as a chaplain. His work there included giving retreats, and he seemed very happy at it. Once he wrote: "In spite of old age, bad eyes and general decrepitude, I was assigned to give the eight-day retreat at our novitiate near St. Louis. There were about fifty, mostly lay brothers. These, as you know, are simple and devout men who enter religion and do not aspire to the priesthood but devote themselves to the humble duties of the house. They lead a very peaceful life without the worries and responsibilities of the priestly duties. We finished on the feast of the Purification.

"It was a real pleasure to receive your letters and to spend a little time with each of you and share the many joys God gives us in His goodness, even if sometimes, for very good reason, He permits a few crosses to come upon us. As one of you said, He sends crosses only to those who can bear them. I can add—He sends crosses only to those whom He trusts to profit by them, and whom He loves in a special manner. Since this is true, how very happy each one of us should be."

One day when John Paul was feeling his blackest and lost in his old doubts and uncertainties for a while again, Lorenzo wrote: "We all must have those days when we are ready to give up, as I know I seem to get a blue day once in a while, but I can't find a reason for it. Our Lord isn't going to appear to give us a renewal of our patience and courage, so we must try to reach Him by mental prayer and meditation.

"I listened to the Mass for shut-ins on the radio this morning, and it had me thinking of the hard struggle the ones Christ picked to carry on for Him had, and how our Lord preferred to let them do it the hard way when He could very easily have made their work much easier.

"So if we, the sick, are part of all this, it is easier to

85

understand why our path must not be made too easy for us. Some years ago I was fortunate enough to have a visit from a Cistercian monk, which is unusual, and in the course of our talk he said he envied me my chance to serve God in the way I had been chosen to do so. For one who had lived a life of sacrifice to say that made me feel that there was a good reason for all of this. One thing the monk said to me that I'll never be able to forget, and it left me very curious. He said "When you think of heaven, don't expect you are going to see anything you have seen in this world."

Miss Grey had commented on that, quoting from St. Paul who was a favorite of hers. "No," she agreed, " 'for eye has not seen, ear has not heard, nor has it entered the heart of man to know what wonders God has prepared for those who love Him.' "

Another time Claire wrote: "Michael lost his job in New York and has not had much luck yet locating anything steady. We are expecting our cherub in November and are delighted at the prospect of having our very own baby to care for and watch grow. Despite my doctor's warning not to have children, I am doing pretty well, proving their theory wrong and my faith and trust in God right. The fact that this will be a Holy Year baby thrills me even more. Please say a prayer that all will go well for us."

Jerry wrote a story his sister Mary had written about him that round, and John Paul liked it:

"The Lucky Ones

"Once there was a happy little boy in our block. He didn't have much to make him happy, not half so much as half of us. He was an invalid and lived all day in the same chair on the same porch in the same house. But he smiled at us 'lucky ones' mornings when we went to work. *Poor boy*, we thought—and we came home from our work in dirty, crowded trains—but he was still smiling. How dull a day he had—no work to do, no meetings of friends, none of these things that meant life to us 'lucky ones.'

"Our little crippled boy had none of these, he just sat and watched, and he dreamed and smiled.

"He watched the trees, he heard the branches rustling through the summer, and his heart sang when autumn came. He watched the sunlight and knew how the clouds piled up high before a storm. He saw the first snowflakes fall and watched the ice-covered wires transformed into filaments of gold.

"He watched us 'lucky ones'—we never knew how closely. He saw our morning hopefulness and our weariness at night. He guessed our sorrows hidden behind our smiles, and that somehow we really saw very little, for all our comings and goings. And as he grew, he came to see a Plan to life, and he was very happy then. It gave his life joy; it filled all his being, and all the things he had seen came alive in it. Spring memories and all the hidden songs of his heart came alive and were poems too!

"He saw everything in a new light—the tragedies, triumphs, the ceaseless coming and going he had watched, took on new meaning; they were stories to him, countless stories, humorous, pathetic, and pervading them all there was a deep love for mankind. A love that was part of a Greater Love he had come to know.

"There is a very joyful man on our block; he suffers much, and cannot leave his chair. Strangers, seeing him, whisper: 'Poor man,' and as they hurry by think, 'Aren't we fortunate? Aren't we the lucky ones!'

"But we are silent. Lucky ones? Are we? Poor, poor blind ones!"

"How do you like that story?" Jerry asked. "Here is more from 'Operation Lourdes' too, to help you understand how I can be happy, not being cured:

"Today we saw our first horror cases. According to what we had read, we had expected to see many terrible sights; but so far, most of the sick people, even though they are not able to walk, have looked quite healthy. However, today in the baths there was one man who had a terrible purple-colored birthmark all over one side of his face. Mary saw him before he went into the baths. She says he is a *brancardier**. I didn't see the second one myself, but Mary can't get over it. It was a baby about two or three years old with a horrible skin infection all over his face and head. The general color of his skin was blue, but his whole face and head were covered with yellow- and greenish- colored scabs and sores. The contours of his face were unharmed. Mary said he was chubby and had a cute nose. He didn't seem to be suffering, either. He was playing with some bits of colored paper and seemed quite content, but Mary said she couldn't get his face out of her mind.

"Then, while we were waiting in line for the blessing of the sick, we saw another bad case. It was a little girl about eight years old who apparently could see but who seemed quite out of her mind. She was lying on a stretcher, and her entire body kept twitching in such a way that her head and shoulders kept rising from the pillow, and she seemed to be rocking back and forth. Her mother sat on a little

* *Brancardiers:* the volunteers who carry the sick at Lourdes on stretchers or push the wheel chairs.

88

stool beside the stretcher. She was a thin, weary-eyed wisp of a woman. She kept trying to calm the little girl. Finally she picked her up in her arms and began walking with her. The little girl seemed almost as big as she. Then she brought her back and laid her down again. The child had been whimpering, but now she started to giggle in fits. Her eyes kept rolling upward, and she kept reaching out her hands aimlessly.

"The poor mother looked as if she had not slept in weeks.

"Today neither Mary nor I had the heart to pray for my cure. Mary said that when she saw those others, and thought how comparatively easy it is to take care of me, she felt like thanking Him for the privilege of being allowed to take care of me for so many years. She said that, during the blessing, she felt that Mother was very close and that she could look up to her and tell her honestly that all was well, and that she need never, never fear. Mother was always so afraid I would be a burden to Mary.

"After the blessing we went to the grotto. On the way there we met two *brancardiers* carrying a stretcher. On the stretcher was a middle-aged woman who seemed to be half laughing and half crying. A crowd of people followed after them, pushing and talking excitedly. It seems the woman had just been cured and was being brought to the medical bureau. Then later, when we got to the grotto and were praying there, we saw a man climbing up to where the crutches are, to hang up a plaster cast of half a leg and foot—another cure! We also noticed another corsetlike contrivance shaped like a vest which was not there yesterday."

Then Jerry had told how there were twelve miraculous cures that week. That had delighted John Paul and Miss

Grey, and they had marveled at God's goodness and mercy to men.

Another time they had been speaking in the group about poverty, and Jerry had included another sheet from his Lourdes diary—this time about Carmen, a good friend he had made while there.

"Carmen came to see us this afternoon. She came right into the room and we had a nice visit. She is such a warm, lovely and deeply religious person. She really must have suffered a great deal during the war. She was trying to explain to us how your attitude changes when you are desperately in need of things. She says that is something she never can make her aunts in New York realize. They are sympathetic and want to help, but so often they send useless things.

"Her explanation to them was something like this: First when you see people picking up things in the street you think to yourself: 'What a terrible thing—how far they have fallen!' and you are sure that, no matter how poor you might become, you would never do such a thing yourself.

"However, after you have gone many days without the things you need, you say to yourself, when you see others picking things up, 'I'd have liked to pick that up myself.'

"Soon you find that when you see a scrap of wool, or a bit of food, or anything you can use, you look around to see if anyone is watching, then you snatch it up quickly. If you have gone without long enough, you don't care. Carmen says she has gotten to the point where she doesn't miss a thing on the road. Everything can be used in some way, and everything is so scarce."

Neither John Paul nor Miss Grey needed Jerry's comments on that passage. It was poverty that looked across the miles and spoke to them. And war too. John Paul had never thought very much about poverty before; now he thought about it. He had never thought much about war either. Such things had seemed so remote and unreal. Now suddenly they were clothed in flesh and faced him.

"God, give the whole world peace," he said, "especially for the sake of the poor, who are most like You in the way they have to live."

Best of all, John Paul liked these excerpts from "Operations Lourdes," as Jerry called his diary. John Paul liked the passages written at Paray-le-Monial especially. Many nights when his pain was bad and his mood black as the night outside, he took comfort in these passages and found strength as well as consolation in them.

On these nights he felt terribly alone, with a peculiar loneliness that seemed somehow to alienate him from all those around him who would have tried to comfort him if they knew. Those moments, even his friend Miss Grey had no part in, and he would not talk about them to her. How could he? There were no words, really, but those of madness or despair. Suppose there was no God? Suppose men were born and lived and struggled and died for a lying hope of an immortality that never was nor could be? Was a life of joy in achievement, and a life of helpless suffering, equally a mockery of the hope men held for themselves and their children? The blackness rolled over and over him, burying him in it so that it was with relief that he took refuge in his physical pain from this mental torment.

It was in moments like these that he thought of Jerry, when he could force his mind to rational thought and push away from it that other thing that crouched over it, feeding it lies to maim and kill. If Jerry, who had also known this pain and desolation that sometimes bordered on despair, could write so, then he too would give faith a chance. He often meditated on the things Jerry wrote:

"Today has been one of the most wonderful days of our entire trip," Jerry had said, in a passage written at Paray. "I only wish we had known about Paray sooner. I wish we had many more days to spend here. The core and heart of it is the very lovely chapel of the Sisters of the Visitation. Here it was that Our Lord appeared many times to St. Margaret Mary Alacoque.

"And here it is that He seems to be more vibrantly present than any place else on earth. Of course Our Lord is in all our churches, but in Paray you feel His presence.

"As you enter the little chapel you seem to be bathed in love and peace.

"It is a feeling I have experienced nowhere else, no, not even in Lourdes. I felt that I would be content to stay there forever. The 'spell' of Paray has attracted many others also. . . . The very air above Paray seems to be especially blessed.

"After Benediction I asked Mary to wheel me over to St. Margaret Mary's altar. Her body is in a glass reliquary. It is perfectly preserved, even though she died in the seventeenth century. She is dressed in the black habit of her order and looks for all the world as if she is just sleeping there. As I sat by the altar I felt as if I, too, were waiting patiently there with her for the great coming of Our Lord. I hated to leave.

"After we had been there a little while the chaplain came out with the relic of St. Margaret Mary. He came over to us and explained that he was going to consecrate us to the Sacred Heart. It was the biggest moment of all our trip. There, at the feet of St. Margaret Mary, we were being consecrated to Our Lord, who loved her so well that He chose her to be the instrument through which He would reveal to the world the mystery and wonder of His Sacred Heart. As Mary said, you simply cannot pray for a miracle at Paray. From the moment you enter the chapel you become vividly aware of Our Lord and of His love for men. You are humbly grateful to be there. Your only thought is that you hope God will make you remember these moments always, and that He will help you to know Him better and to love Him more. All else is in His hands. Nothing else seems to matter. If only that wonderful experience will remain vividly in our memories always . . . this pilgrimage will have marked us in a special way. We have come because we know we need help. We have learned to leave it up to our Blessed Mother and Our Lord to decide what will help us most. When we return home we don't want to be the same two adventurers who left so many weeks ago. We hope with all our hearts that what we have experienced will remain with us always. Please God it may act as a leaven in us. We know that the real end of this book will not be written when we arrive in New York once more. It may not be written for years to come, but we hope that when it is time to write about the real end of our pilgrimage the final pages will be happy ones. There have been so many things we could not understand. So often we have felt bewildered, and sometimes have nearly despaired. And yet we know with great certainty that we have been well guarded and guided throughout our journey. How else could everything have run with such marvelous smoothness? God's ways are so inscrutable! We know there must be some reason for all that has happened, but it became increasingly apparent that the reason may not become clear to us for a long, long time. This afternoon, however, in the chapel at

Paray, we were able to offer up again all the days of our pilgrimage and to ask Our Lord to accept and bless them. We have put ourselves in His keeping. We pray that from here on we shall be guided in His way."

In those moments of darkness, John Paul would utter the same prayer—and with it came always a certain peace, the same peace he knew Jerry Filan had felt when he wrote those words. It was not the unnameable peace that came in his prayer, that wordless Something which he was beginning to accept as his prayer, but a conscious peace and quiet of spirit that was consolation without struggle, which he felt acutely and could express.

VIII. The Lord
Is My Shepherd

The next months were for the most part happy ones for John Paul. The new orderly was decent and John Paul liked him. He was a young fellow and intended to go to medical school next year on the G. I. bill, but meanwhile he worked as an orderly. He wanted to be a doctor and was saving for that. Some of the smart alecs around the hospital made fun of that, and John Paul heard more than one dirty joke that made his face flame in anger.

John Paul said to him more than once, "You'll make it, Gregory, I know you will make it. You have the hands for it."

And he did, long, graceful hands, delicate and deft of touch. And he was gentle as a woman, yet wholly masculine. There was no trace of femininity in his make-up.

He would talk to John Paul a lot when he wasn't busy, and he understood something of suffering. "The way I have it figured," he said once, "everything in the world has to reach a balance, to keep things going. Say it's God, or the plan of creation, whatever you will, but everything keeps trying to reach a balance.

"There is on one side greed, selfishness, exploitation, waste and hate, enough to pull the whole world apart if it were left unchecked; but against those things there is the voluntary resignation of the poor, the sick and all the heavily burdened of the world, always pulling mightily, the sufferings of the innocent, and the sacrifices of those who love greatly, to pull it back into order and reason. You know, John, your job in the world is really just as important as mine, only it is a lot harder. Your job is to love patiently and bear the misunderstanding of others and your own weakness well. Mine is to work and to leave the world a little cleaner or a little saner because I worked."

That made John Paul feel good, and he told Miss Grey about it. "Gregory must be fine," she said.

Another day John Paul told Gregory about CUSA, because the letter had come and Miss Grey was away on vacation. Since it couldn't be fitted onto his book-stand, he could not read it himself. Although he knew Gregory was not a Catholic, he believed he would understand about the letter better than anyone else he knew. At first when John Paul asked him, Gregory protested a little: "But you know I'm not a Catholic, John."

"But it won't be your letter you're writing, but mine. You understand about suffering and things, so I wouldn't mind your reading it to me. There is no one else I could ask. Please, Greg."

"Well, since you put it like that, I guess I'll have to. But I hope your friends won't mind."

"Oh, I don't think they will. They would like you, I'm sure, if they knew you."

So Greg read the letters that round for John Paul and answered them in the words John Paul dictated. That was the month Claire's baby died. John Paul knew he would never forget that letter.

"Dear Father and Friends,

"I have been guilty of delaying the group letter for too long. Please forgive me one and all.

"To begin with, I had my sweet little girl on November 10, but God chose to take her to Himself on the 12th. Needless to say, Michael and I feel such a deep sense of loss at not having Mary Melody with us. We had looked forward to caring for her, having the pleasure of teaching her all the wonderful things that can be taught. But God wanted our baby and we are resigned to His will. Of course we are so earthbound that hurt is there, and I still long to hold my little cherub again.

"God was good to me though, and the Blessed Mother was with me all the time. My doctor had promised me I could see my baby immediately, and so he sent for Michael when it was time for the baby to be born. Michael was with me immediately afterwards, and we held and touched our angel just for a few moments. We never saw her after that. She weighed eight pounds and three ounces and was a lovely, perfectly formed child.

"At birth the cord twisted around her and cut off her circulation just long enough to do fatal damage. Doctor Smith baptized her in the delivery room, as they had a hard time getting Melody to breathe. She finally did—but, oh, such weak little cries. I can remember how quiet her cries were. But it didn't occur to me anything was wrong. Dr. Smith sent for a specialist, and they worked on the baby until Sunday morning. She seemed to gain strength Saturday. But that night she began to fail and died Sunday morning around seven-fifteen. It was a shock to say the least. . . . But we know we have a little saint in heaven praying for us. I miss my little girl dreadfully and beg of all of you to pray for us. I feel bewildered and so empty just now.

"Excuse me, dear friends, for not writing more. I appreciate your prayers for us, and I know our dear infant daughter will pray for you all. It is comforting knowing she can intercede for us. Michael sends his thanks also for your many prayers. A Merry Christmas to each of you, and I'll remember all of you especially in my Mass on December eighth, our CUSA birthday."

Jerry hadn't been able to write much during the past month because his condition had grown much worse. But he did answer that beautifully. They were all glad he could, and more so later in the year when there was more sad news, this time of Jerry himself. In December, his nurse secretary wrote for him: "An electric heater was put too close to his chair. It set fire to the airfoam cushion he sits on and his chair. I was not with him at the time, only his sister was in the house. She did not smell anything until Jerry's room became filled with acrid smoke—Jerry was unable to call for help, as he is unable to speak above a whisper. When his sister finally got to him, she quickly carried him out of his chair onto the bed, and fortunately I arrived at that moment.

"Jerry's arm was severely burned, second-degree burns, and we took care of him, and I called the doctor. All of this was a shock to him, for as you know he had been gravely ill for many months.

"Christmas came and went but Jerry is not too conscious of what goes on about him. I trimmed a Christmas tree for him in his room and a crib. In a few wakeful moments, he looks at them, but interest in all things is gone. He is now too weak to think of anything. I know this news will grieve his many CUSA friends, and may I ask all of you to please pray for him?"

98

John Paul thought how different his own Christmas had been, and the feeling was a strange one. For him, this had been the first real Christmas he had known in his life. Miss Grey had come back from her vacation and had fixed him a little crib on his bedside table. Hospital rules wouldn't permit a tree, so she had fixed him one in her own home, and she and Gregory had taken him there together. A nice young social worker in the hospital had helped them to plan the surprise together. They had fixed brightly wrapped Christmas presents for him and for a stranger to him, an old man Gregory called "Mr. Tex," from another ward. He was not really poor, but he was very lonely, as he had no family or friends. Gregory was always trying to think of ways to make him more comfortable and happy, just as he did for John Paul. The five of them sang Christmas carols together, and John Paul noted with a delighted pride that his own voice was no worse than the cracked piping of old Mr. Tex. And it didn't matter anyway, because they sang to express their joy, not to display their art—which was just as well at that. Afterwards, there was a good dinner which Miss Grey and the social worker had fixed, turkey and cranberries, and all the trimmings.

When John Paul got back to the hospital that night, he was so delightfully tired and stuffed and so full of joy that even the pain was better and he went to sleep at once.

In January, they learned that Jerry was no better, in fact in a whole week he had had only about an hour of consciousness. But during that hour, Dee, his secretary, said she read him the group letter and "he listened very reverently and said his life had been made much richer for being a member of CUSA and knowing such wonderful courageous friends." That made them all feel good, even through the sadness of knowing Jerry was no better.

Margie's letter was cheerful, the children had a happy Christmas and that counted most with her. Lucille's letter was warm too, and cheerful. Her big family had all been home and the children had filled the house with work and laughter. There were several nieces and nephews, one of them a brand new baby. As usual there was a verse to end her letter, and John Paul smiled at it because down in southern Missouri she could still talk about flowers when up here everything was ice and snow.

> I planted in my garden space
> a diary to record on earth
> the friendly ways of folk I know
> in flowers gay that bloom with mirth.
> A golden lily like the smile
> you gave to me that sunny day,
> and lilacs sweet with their perfume
> to scent your path across the way.
> This growing book reveals each page
> of memories that bless and bloom,
> and when I read each blossom through . . .
> How can there be a day of gloom?

Florence wrote about her work at school:

"The experience here at the college is invaluable. This is the only college in the world for the deaf. Of course many deaf boys and girls attend the regular colleges and universities, but always laboring under the handicap. Here there is no handicap, as all are alike and conditions meet their special needs. John Paul, you mention your grief in not being able to attend Mass. I did some thinking on that subject when I was in a wheel chair and I happened to remember St. John the Baptist. Except for the time he baptized our Lord, I believe he was never physically close to Him.

Yet how very close spiritually. He never had Him as close as we do in Holy Communion, yet he was a saint.

"Now I'll step down from the pulpit. Yes, I have a full life, but I also have my problems.

"And now to our leader, who was in pain when he wrote to us. Think of what our freedom from pain will mean to us some day! Isn't it winning over obstacles that makes life interesting? Whether these obstacles are getting a hand or foot back in use or winning over pain.

"By the next time I'll have my job under better control and can more easily let my mind wander to my friends, so I won't hold the letter for so long. Prayers for you all."

Father S. wrote: "May the good merciful Lord grant each one of you His richest and most abundant graces during the New Year. Unfortunately, because of weak eyes and a good bit of extra work, the two or three weeks prior to Christmas I did not send each one of you a personal note as I had planned. I never believed in expensive cards with just a name printed. For a number of years I sent these personal notes—I know they have helped to prove to my friends how much I esteemed them. One of my Christmas Masses was offered for all my friends, and thus you were included.

"I am so glad our group of letters are making such good time, and to me they bring so much that is interesting and awakens the sincere desire that God give you all great courage and a real abundance of His richest favors and His choicest graces.

"Somehow I have always felt that the real dynamos of power with God to win souls and carry on His work for souls are not only priests and active missionaries, not only the good sisters themselves who immolate themselves by a life of sacrifice in teaching unruly children or caring for cranky sick people in hospitals, but also the good lay people who suffer. Suffering is an apostolate which requires no very great sanctity, just a bit of resignation to God's will, just a little wisdom to see His hand in everything, just a little love for Him to enable us to offer our ordinary ailments with a simple and devout heart to God. Personally, I have a great deal for which to be very thankful to almighty God. Even lately the almost complete restoration of my sight which enables me to do ever so many things for the benefit of others is a blessing for which I feel most grateful.

"May the loving and most adorable Heart of our Blessed Savior continue blessing each one of you and filling you even to overflowing with His sweetest consolation."

Part of Lorenzo's letter was an answer to the question someone in the group had asked for general discussion, "What has been hardest about your sickness?":

"Pain might seem the first thing to come to mind, and although I would not like to go through some of my roughest periods again, as I look back I do think that having another do all things for you is very hard, as you can't help but feel at times that they are annoyed, which is bound to happen as they don't always feel too good themselves. Patience and courage, to me, is the real secret to everything. If we can hold our courage to face the day-to-day sufferings and have the patience to bear them just one more day and pray that Christ will give us the strength to get to the next day, then it is always sure to give us a better outlook.

"I received the group letter the day after Christmas, and it was like adding another gift to my Christmas presents. Oh, yes, my family and friends were most generous, and I received some gifts that were so welcome. My sisters gave me a Parker 51 pen, which I am now using and hope that it will be my answer to a very annoying problem. I was so sorry to read that we had so many not feeling well this round. I do hope and will pray that a new year will bring better health to the group.

"I know many of you are members of the Shut-in League and are familiar with Mary Ellen Kelly, the leader. On December 16 I received a telephone call from another shut-in telling me she had heard Mary Ellen on the radio program 'Welcome, Travelers' and that she would be on television in a few days. On the 19th she was on, and it was a real thrill to see her and hear her talking as though she had been in my room with me."

When he answered the letter, John Paul, after answering the others, told of his own happy Christmas and answered the question for general discussion: "I agree with Lorenzo, having others do everything for you is worse than the pain. Another thing that is hard is the solitude, being alone, feeling that no one really understands, and yourself always asking why, and receiving no answer, or not wanting to accept the answer received."

He was thinking of George then, and some of the other orderlies and nurses like him, and of something Jerry had said long ago in one of his letters: "Someone very dear to me misunderstands me very much. I have even been accused of letting my body get into this horrible condition."

John Paul had had similar experiences, not from his loved ones, for few had ever loved him and these had understood, but from tired orderlies and a few social workers who were thoughtless or tactless.

"Having people pity you is hard," he went on, "but it is equally hard to have them find you guilty, in their minds, of the *crime* of being sick and helpless, as if somehow it were your own fault and you could change it if you willed, and won't. I have found that hardest as a charity patient in an institution."

In February, Jerry died. He died quietly and swiftly; he had suffered a great deal before. The head of CUSA wrote a letter to the group telling of his death, and expressing the grief of the whole American CUSA at the death of its first member. "Jerry is our saint. You have read parts of his journal and know what a marvelous soul he was. May I propose something to have him remembered, not only by those Cusans who had the privilege to know him but all the others in CUSA today and in later days? You all know that the eighteenth of each month is the day when all members should offer their prayers and pain for the spiritual and temporal good of CUSA. It was the custom in the French Union and became the custom in other countries. Now here is the reason why that special day was chosen. A French officer, Charles Rheinhardt, was the first member of the Catholic Union to go to heaven, and he died on the 18th of May, 1914. The founders of the Union thought it would be fine to commemorate what they called their first link with heaven.

"Now Jerry is not our first member who went home to God, but he was the first American member of the Catholic Union, as Father Finn is its first chaplain. Do you not think it would be fine to have here in America the fourth, instead of the eighteenth, chosen as that day offered each month for our Union? Jerry will join us on that day especially."

And so it came about that American Cusans began to observe the fourth day of each month for the spiritual and temporal good of the American CUSA. The holy hour was to be held on that day also, in memory of Jerry.

But meanwhile, John Paul remembered Jerry's letter just before he went to Lourdes:

"God and Our Lady have to help me some way. . . . I don't see how I can continue this way of life."

Yes, God and Our Lady had helped him, after all, in the most perfect way possible. They had taken him to themselves to share their own lives in peace and happiness forever, that knew no pain nor suffering. John Paul was glad for Jerry.

IX. All the Way
To Heaven

In a few months Jerry's father, John Luke Filan, took Jerry's place in the group. In his first letter he said, "I am only sixty-one years old, and two years ago, the first time in life that I was ever sick, I had a heart attack—confined to bed for three months. The doctor said I would have to stop working and that I would never be able to handle Jerry again, but I did both, and only by faith and prayer. . . . Pause here for three Our Fathers in honor of God the Father, Son and Holy Ghost for all the members of CUSA and the sick folks all over the world. Faith is such a wonderful thing, and it's a terrifying thought to be without it.

"Where do I work? I thought you knew. Well, I'm the Long Island supervisor of Catholic Charities Salvage, and right now we are nearly finished sending overseas about sixty-five tons of clothes and canned food collected by all the churches in the Long Island end of the diocese.

"It's two o'clock in the morning, and I'm blinking and nodding, and I suppose making mistakes here and there.

"Forgot to tell you my wife Adelaide died six years ago and my daughter and her husband and three children live with me. My wife was an invalid the last three years of her life, and I have had a little party of troubles too, but as the Jewish saying goes, 'If we put down our bag of troubles

106

and pick up the next man's bag, we will be glad to pick up and exchange for our own.'

"Good morning,
"John Luke Filan."

John Paul liked that letter from his namesake and felt sure he was going to like him fine. During those months he felt deeply for Claire. She was the answer to those who think that for some there is an easy path to sanctity. He had heard them: "Well, it's her temperament, you know, a nice placid, happy temperament like that, it's easy to be a saint. Things just don't bother them like they do other people. They don't really suffer."

He knew it wasn't true, and he shared in Claire's suffering as he knew she and all his little family shared in his as they tried to help and encourage each other in this growing in grace and tender patient nursing of the Christ-life in them.

Yet he knew, too, that it is in our suffering that we are sanctified. There is no other way than the cross; Our Lord told us that long ago. If there had been a better way, He would certainly have chosen it. He knew too that mental suffering, the suffering caused by temptation and fears and such like, is a big part of the cross a Christian must carry—quite as big a part as that other suffering with which He was so familiar, the pains of the body.

Once Claire wrote: "It was nice receiving the group letter again. I haven't been able to answer it until tonight though. I am glad most of the group are doing well. Progress seems to be the high note of the letters.

"Thanks for your prayers, everyone. I need them. I can't pray myself. My faith in people and everything has been shaken.

"I took a dictaphone course and am now looking for

work. Work and more work seems to be the only solution to my confusion and emotional turmoil. I doubt if I'll find any, but I'm looking. In the meantime, I'm doing most anything to get away from the apartment. I gave a talk at a luncheon Saturday and have been on television twice and was with the mayor of our city and had my pictures taken for the official opening of 'Week for the Blind.' Keeping busy keeps one from thinking.

"Michael is well and gaining his much-needed poundage back. He was thirty pounds underweight two months ago. I have some weight-gaining to do myself. However, generally speaking we are all right. I'm thankful for Michael's job. It has been a long time in coming.

"I won't write a long letter this time. I haven't much to contribute; certainly my present attitude can't add a thing to this very spiritual group. I hope you all will stay well and keep us in your prayers. We appreciate all you have said. I've entrusted your intentions with Melody. She does my praying for me."

John Paul knew it was hard, and Father S. must have known it, too, because though his message was meant for them all, and had some special meaning for each of them, John Paul thought it full of the hope that would be specially consoling to Claire at that time. The best part of what he said was a quote from Father Finn, from an article he had written in the bulletin, or CUSA newsletter:

"Before the gospel of the fifth Sunday after Easter we have an account of one of the last talks of Our Lord with His apostles. He told them: 'A little while and you shall not see me, and again a little while you shall see me, and your sorrow shall be turned into joy and your joy no man shall take from you; for whatever you shall ask the Father in My

108

Name shall be granted you. Ask and receive, that your joy may be full.'

"Our Lord definitely had in mind spiritual favors to be granted when He spoke these words to the apostles, but He did not exclude temporal ones, for He granted many such temporal favors all through His public life in His tremendous sympathy and mercy towards humanity.

"In a few short hours after His last talk He would Himself be praying in Gethsemane for relief from the bitter torment of the Passion. But these subsidiary requests are all conditional. In His agony in the garden He gave the principle 'Not My will but Thine be done.'

"In our restricted outlook we are very poor judges, even in the temporal sphere, of what is really to our advantage. Those of us who have a fairly long experience of life will remember that many of the things we set our hearts on were only the preludes to disaster, and that our deeply felt 'disappointments' just saved us from disaster. With all eternity in view, we are still more likely to be misguided, like little glow-worms measuring our lights against the glory of the sun at noon-day. We are like the little child who asks his nurse for the blade he sees gleaming in the morning sunshine. If she agrees, he may many, many years after have to say to his friends: 'My foolish request was granted. That is why my forehead is scarred and my sight gone, and why these poor fingers of mine are paralyzed.'

"Christ's final statement in this gospel is a glorious basis of unlimited confidence in Him. It is a condensed declaration of His glorious existence, of His death and resurrection and final triumph. In His name we can secure anything we really want—the temporal blessings that are not obstacles to salvation and the grace of God that will give us a place forever with Christ and the Comforter, the Paraclete He promised. That Divine Comforter, abiding now with the Mystical Body of Christ forever, comes to our door particularly at Confirmation, bringing with Him the seven gifts of the Holy Ghost to endow us with the spirit of Christ, the wisdom, the fortitude to face reality. He did not run away from the cross, He knew it was inevitable. We are often tempted to run away from reality to liquor and drugs, night clubs and other escapes, but they don't bring happiness. Escape to pleasure is not escape to happiness. We need to call with confidence and faith on those gifts of wisdom and fortitude that are ours in meeting the realities of life. The saints live by faith and pray with it and wisdom."

The next month Claire wrote that the group letter was indeed a welcome one this time. "Generally speaking, everyone seems pretty good. I'm glad for that. Father, your letter was so inspiring. Surely you could use it for a sermon some Sunday. The idea could fit anyone's life.

"As I write, I am playing a record, 'The King and I,' with the original cast singing the songs. It was a house gift from a singer friend, and I have played the record over and over again. The songs are so delightful, and often the words have such a beautiful meaning. One of my favorites is 'Getting to Know You.' I'd love to see this show. My friend Gladys from Brooklyn is going to try to get tickets for June. If I can make the trip, I surely will go. I often play my records when here alone. It helps fill the loneliness I often experience. Loneliness is such a heavy cross at times. Vicky is such a help though. She is working fine and is used to her new home now.

"Our apartment is truly lovely, with large rooms, all freshly painted, and ample closet space. Our kitchen is nice and large too, and it is a pleasure to cook in it. The park out back is so nice too. It is almost like having a private yard. Vicky and I sit out there and are trying to get some color in our faces. Vicky doesn't look pale exactly, but she is recovering too. She hasn't been well all winter, but the doctor says it's all a reflection from me. I dearly love my hound and would be so lost without her.

"I'm working with a guild, and it is coming along fine. It is growing so fast. They have a discussion club which meets twice a month and a choral group. They have a book review occasionally and other activities. One of our prospects is passing out a little circular with blue ribbon on it, and the idea of the club is to fight the red badge of Communism with the blue ribbon of Mary. A Rosary is required each day for membership. There is a fee of one dollar, but that isn't essential.

"On Monday Michael, Gladys and I went to see a blind couple and their two-month-old daughter. I hadn't seen Marie since her birth. She is a dear child and very good. My blind friend takes care of her by herself and is doing a fine job. We had both planned on our babies together, and I passed Melody's things on to her. I have so much, and it is a shame for those things to lie in drawers, unused. I felt bad of course, at holding her baby; it sure made me miss my own so much. Both Michael and I came home with tears in our hearts. Six months hasn't helped heal the hurt.

"Have any of you read *The Mysteries of the Rosary*, by Msgr. Sheen? They are exquisite! If I ever get back on the path with all you good people, it will be through your prayers I know, but also through the meditations of Msgr. Sheen. The fourth mystery of the Joyful is what hit home with me. I am having copies Brailled for myself and a few friends. The Rosary is so hard for me to say. I hardly pray— I pretty nearly always end up in tears. But I think of you

111

when I make my morning offering and hope that will cover it.

"To the kitchen I must go now. It is ten after seven, and I must be Martha if I am to keep a happy hubby . . . Michael isn't looking well at all. Mother tells me he is a bad color. I guess this has been a hard winter on him too—especially putting up with me.

"Well, my best to all. Hope the next letter finds everyone improving and happy."

The whole tone of that letter was so much happier than the one before it, that John Paul rejoiced. He remembered something the new priest had said to him once in one of those black moments when discouragement was upon him, and he could not pray—or at least he did not think he could pray. "Don't worry about that at all, John Paul, it is not at all what it seems," he had told him. "Don't you realize that these troubled thoughts, this mental anguish caused by what you call your inability to pray, this tortured striving for prayer and the sufferings of your efforts in that direction, are themselves the most perfect prayer you can offer and the most effective ones in drawing down God's grace upon yourself? The desire to pray is prayer and meritorious of grace. God loves those efforts, John Paul."

He wrote that in his letter to her and hoped it would be consolation for her, as it had been for him. Once more, Father S.'s letter was encouraging to all of them. Besides this he had joyous news for them to share with him that month. "In a few days I am celebrating my golden jubilee as a Religious," he said. "As soon as the rush of the celebration is over I will send our members a little note. In the meantime, I am enclosing memorial pictures."

Florence was well and still very busy: "Again I am taking out a page or two and sticking them in my trusty typewriter," she said, "and a brand new machine it is. I hope you will all stand around and admire its work, overlooking errors that result from human imperfection (meaning me!). My old machine is about thirty-five years old, so I'm turning it out to pasture to end its days in peace. It served me fifteen years.

"Now for a brief message to each of you—I say brief because this job of mine has me in a corner. I'd love to tell you all about it, but if I started I'd need more time than I have and much more space than we are allowed. Maybe next time.

"Have you noticed in the hospital how many wonderful people turn up in such places? I find this among the handicapped—the deaf and the blind particularly. I'll always be thankful to God for letting me know so many people with courage almost beyond belief.

"Yes, Claire, I love my work and it is good to know that, out of my own experience with a handicap, I can help others to surmount theirs.

"Lorenzo, I read about the meeting of the Holy Name Society there and imagine it was an inspiring sight. We had something along that order here at the Washington Monument, with Father Peyton himself the principal speaker. Archbishop O'Boyle was also present and addressed the vast multitude.

"And now, John—do the rest of you know that I keep John busy with the Little Flower in my behalf? In fact, I'm leaving a big problem in his hands right now and depending on his influence with the Little Flower to see it through.

"You ask about my close companion, the cane. I'm afraid I won't dispose of it for a long time, if ever. I just swallow my pride and sally forth between buildings here, cane and all. The young people are very nice about it.

"Father, thank you very much for your beautiful message. It has special appeal for me.

"Now, I'll say goodnight to you all. A remembrance in my prayers and my love."

John Paul only wrote a short note that round because Miss Grey was away again and Gregory was sick. In a short time Gregory would be leaving anyway, going to school, and John Paul hated to think about it. They were becoming good friends. He often came on the Sundays when he was off duty to take John Paul for a ride in his car. When Miss Grey was off, sometimes she went too, and the three of them had lots of fun. Gregory knew just how to go about helping John Paul, feeding him, lifting him, changing his position in a way that was matter-of-fact, yet which at the same time somehow conveyed that he was being *privileged* to do those things. He did not make John Paul feel as if he was a burden, or as if he ought to show gratitude and appreciation for every little thing. And for that very reason, John Paul was the more grateful and appreciative.

During the round that followed, Father S. suggested, as Florence had suggested before then, that they discuss books in the group letter, like a real discussion group, each reading and exchanging ideas on books.

"My work here is entirely different from my job of the last four years. It does not require so much physical effort, and yet is productive of good. We aim at forming model Catholic laymen, real leaders, well-equipped mentally and in character to carry on a veritable apostolate for Christ Our Lord. To help form good leaders seems a slow process, yet the results are very evident. You all by your prayers, and above all by your patience and resignation in your afflictions and even joy in bearing your crosses, can help in a wonderful manner."

"You see, John Paul," Miss Grey told him as she read that part, "it is something that has to be reaffirmed again and again, yet we know it is true. Your work is here, lying in this bed or sitting in this chair, offering your helplessness and sufferings to God. It is hard work, and there is little pay sometimes in this life, we know, but you have to go on believing there is more than this, and your pay, when it comes, will be great."

"I believe that," John Paul answered, "and hard as I find it to pray or to understand my own prayer—there is something, when I make the effort, Miss Grey, especially of late, that makes me know we don't have to wait until then for everything. Even here, I begin to see the beginnings of God's Kingdom. I don't know how to say it, I feel foolish trying to talk about it to someone else, especially to someone like you who probably know more about it than I do anyway.

"But there is *something*. If you love God and keep trying to love Him more and give yourself more to Him and keep trying to understand what His love means, every once in a while He fills you with *something*, something that is light, yet not light, joy, but not exactly joy either, but way beyond it, that fills you sometimes so full you have to ask Him to stop—you can't take any more—yet all the time you are wishing it could go on forever. And you think then—this is what eternity is like. And you feel that you could do anything, bear anything, suffer any pain or hurt or loss if only in the end you might have this forever. Then you know this is love, God's love, and while the knowledge lasts you aren't afraid any more, nothing matters in earth or heaven but that."

He lifted his face anxiously to his friend. "Do you understand what I'm trying to say, Miss Grey? Or is it all confused and mixed-up like most things I say are? I can't explain it at all, sometimes I can't understand it or feel it at all. Then everything is dark and frightening because God won't come to me, and I wonder if maybe I imagined the other. Yet even under all my doubts and the faults and sins I commit because of my doubts, I do know I didn't imagine it, that it is real, and so I keep trying. . . . I keep falling, picking myself up, and starting over as He gives me the grace."

Miss Grey smiled down at the anxious face. "Oh yes, I understand, John Paul," she said. "I understand perfectly. There are lots of names for what you are feeling and describing, but names don't matter. Those who are truly in love with God's will and whose love for Him makes them determined to serve Him perfectly must all suffer such things, and I think will all, from time to time, know that inner something that gives them peace and makes them know that the darkness will pass and that going through it is worth while.

"But now let's get back down to earth, or we will never finish these letters. Here is Florence."

"Dear Friends, I am sorry to have held up the package for so long. I've had it five now—no, seven—days. It will go out this evening.

"This small college graduated thirty-five young men and women, and it hurts to see them go. That is the lot of the teacher who loves her young students. The majority of the graduates I may never see again. But, thinking about that, I remember the many, many people of outstandingly beautiful character who have passed in and out of my life as I travelled about, changing my place of residence and work several times, and whose friendship meant much to me. And I like to think that we gain something from even passing contacts with fine people.

"Another interruption—but a worthy one. A young priest of the nearby parish church has been appointed chaplain of the college Newman Club. During the past year he made a number of friends among the students, and now two of these young people are being married and have asked him to marry them. As the two principals are totally deaf, Father asked me if I would teach him the signs used in the marriage ceremony. So we sat down to it and Father will drop in again on Friday for another session. So it goes, but I am happy to be of service.

"Yes, the summer vacation is now at hand and I'm lined up for several weeks of work with one of the professors who is editor of the American *Annals of the Deaf*. It is a professional publication and requires experience in the particular field for its workers.

"Then I am scheduled for a professional trip out West, but this is no extended sightseeing tour. A few days in San Francisco and then back to Washington by air. Then, on July 16, I am to speak at the International Congress of the Catholic Deaf in Detroit. This will be made up of workers for and with the deaf. I'll drop our leader a card as I leave on each trip, just in case the letters start for me at the time.

"We all know by this time that our present letters were held up along the way, and I'm glad to see that they finally turned up. Our beloved John Luke was quite concerned about them. The pictures enclosed this time are lovely. It is good to be able to 'see' mentally the person we are writing to.

"Those of you who are troubled by those who will not

117

believe you are really sick should read Father McAstocker's book *The Joy of Sorrow*. He treats of just that difficulty along with other aspects of illness and invalidism. But remember, you who are confined to your homes can give so much of yourselves to the cause of peace, through reading and study and prayer. There are no four walls in the world that can imprison the mind or the spirit."

He told Gregory about that when he was feeding him, later, and to his surprise his friend said, "She has something there, John Paul. You know I'm learning a lot from you and your friends, a lot about things I just took for granted I knew and didn't know, before. Don't you be surprised if someone of these mornings when I take you out to Mass, I kneel down beside you for Communion. It will be all right. I've been going to Father Halloran nights lately to learn what it is that makes you and Jean—that is, Miss Grey—and Florence and Claire and all the others, like you are—what makes you different. Maybe I'd like to have a part of it."

John Paul nearly choked on his dinner, he was so surprised and happy. "Boy, would that be swell!" he exclaimed. "I'm sure going to pray for it, Greg."

In another round, Florence's letter said, "We will all be with Father when and if surgery comes. What a beautiful outlook he has and a lovely attitude toward all God is sending.

"Isn't it John Paul who mentions Catherine Doherty's latest book? What a woman! And what a work she has founded! It was she who wrote to me about the deaf Negroes in Harlem. I visited Friendship House and arranged for classes in lipreading for the Negro deaf. Mrs. Doherty was then at the Canadian center. For two years I taught those

118

Negroes weekly and had a chance to observe the way of life in Friendship House. It is something to behold: and to study!

"Now I must leave you and get this in the box before 8:30 when the mail is picked up. My love and prayers all around."

Claire's letters were longer too, and John Paul could see that she was getting her balance again. "Florence," she said in that round, "you sure have a full and interesting life. I can't imagine how you crowd so much in a day. My day begins at six-thirty, and from then till bedtime I push myself to do everything, and little or nothing gets done some days. My admiration goes out to you.

"I'd love to do more for CUSA, but getting mail read and getting it off to the post office has always been a problem. Since I still can't use Vicky as much as I did, I can't depend on her for my every wish.

"My, I am blessed with a few wonderful neighbors. In fact two of the girls did my huge wash for me today, and one of them did quite a bit of the ironing. My iron broke and she knew it, so she took the bulk of the ironing up to her apartment. That is real charity, I think. Washing and ironing can never be a pleasure, but they really do it cheerfully. My strength has not returned, and keeping the apartment clean seems almost too much at times, but Michael can always be proud to walk in at night, as I believe in having a clean home and good meals on the table if nothing else.

"I changed doctors, and think I have hit on one that has the clue to my continued rundown condition. I've had an internal infection for nine months that would not go away. He used some kind of electrical device, and it is clearing up. He made tests and said I am very low and rundown and lacking in vitamins and proteins. He has ordered a new drug for me to take by injection, as well as iron and liver shots too. He is getting the medicine at cost and letting my father, mother and future sister-in-law give me the shots to save expenses. He said I'd never feel right until this infection was cured. He assured me that, despite my own efforts to overcome blue spells, my rundown condition defeats me at every turn. So, here is hoping this is it! I can't recall ever feeling so down in all my life, and I don't want to. I try so hard and rarely cry any more. I realize death is something we cannot change. But poor health and infections coupled with the shock of losing Melody just seemed too much, but I feel improvement and hope I can say much more in my next letter.

"I was very surprised and very pleased to learn Michael had written a letter in my place last time I was on vacation. He writes well, and his writing indicates just what he thinks and what a wonderful man he really is. I am so lucky and always thank God for sending this one beautiful soul into my life.

"I was very much surprised and delighted with my Surprise. The minute my foot touched the kitchen floor I knew it had been fixed up. What a pleasure it is to work with so many conveniences. The vacuum has been a godsend. So much of my cleaning was done on hands and knees and was just too much. Michael continually keeps looking for ways to make life easier and more pleasant. Both of us agree we are closer and more in love than the day we married. I guess we both work at our marriage.

"Father, Michael smiled at reading your message directed at him. He said to tell you he learned his philosophy at the school of 'hard knocks,' but I agree with you he is very Catholic in thought. Only a push is needed, and he will come into the Church. That will be a happy day in our lives for sure.

120

"Mother Abbess, I can imagine how busy you are with all your flock to tend. How do you do it? I thought of you and Father this morning in Mass during the gospel of the Shepherd and one flock. You are truly a counterpart of Him. We are so fortunate in having you visit our group.

"I haven't had time to see the doctor, but I feel so well I will wait a little longer. (It is so good to say I feel well.) My mental outlook is infinitely better. Thanks for everything, Father and friends. I made a good Forty Hours and you were with me there. Prayers come very hard—usually with tears—but the effort is there.

"John Luke, I'm like you. If I don't write letters immediately, I am apt to forget the messages I want to write. When you mention my wedding being a rare thing for shut-ins, it brought home again to me my great blessings! So few shut-ins or handicapped people have the chance to live and love so fully. I have never ceased to thank God for Michael and pray our marriage will always be as precious and beautiful.

"It takes daily watching—like a flower needing water and sunshine. Our tempers clash at times, our viewpoints differ, but always we try to remember that these things are small and unimportant. The important thing to remember is that we are in love for keeps and this union must maintain the dignity God intended.

"John Paul, like you it is difficult to get the letters read at one time. I have apologized so often, I don't any more. I feel all of you understand and forgive—I hope. Michael is so overworked that some evenings I feel I can't ask him to read when he is so tired. He uses his eyes all day and he gets mighty weary by night. He also had a severe ear infection that infected his left jawbone. He suffered a lot working and going to school. Under the care of a good doctor he is fine again. He completes his school term in the middle of August.

"Vicky is doing fairly well in the heat. It does bother her and I've been trying not to take her out on the real hot days. She was badly frightened over the Fourth of July with the firecrackers. Since then, loud noises send her into the shakes. She is almost seven, and her age is beginning to tell. We spent the week-end at my mother's farm and indulged in swimming. Vicky is so cute with me in the water. She swims after me and makes me come in to shore if she thinks I've gone out too far. If I don't go back with her, she starts barking at me.

"She doesn't want me in the water at best, and barks from the shore when I just get in. Then she comes in after me and nudges me with her nose. She is an old silly but very sweet."

It was after this letter that Miss Grey and Gregory told him their news. He wasn't very surprised, he had expected it for some time. And he was very glad for both of them. But he teased them: "It's Claire's letters. They've sold you the married life. You want to try it out for yourself. Tell Claire, when we write again, it's not Harry but she who is playing Cupid around here."

They laughed and Miss Grey blushed. "Well, I just hope our marriage will be as happy as hers, and God willing, it will be, because we are both going to work at it."

"We sure are," Gregory agreed, looking down at her, smiling.

Gregory was baptized in the Catholic Church in August, and he and Miss Grey were married in September, just before he had to go to school.

John Paul wanted to give something, but he had nothing

to give, so he made a poem, and one of the other patients printed it for him on beautiful white paper. They said it was beautiful, and that made him happy. When Father Cole came to bring him his God in Holy Communion, he offered that too, and all his prayers and sufferings of the day. They were pleased, and their thanks sounded genuine and touched.

They went away for a short honeymoon before school started, and while they were away the group letter came. There was no one to read and answer it for him, so John Paul had to send it back. That made him a little sad, but he knew it was only for a short time.

When it came around again, Miss Grey was back. Although now she was Mrs. Calvinski, John Paul still thought of her as Miss Grey.

All their Cusan friends were glad for Gregory and Miss Grey, Claire, Lucille, Marge, Father, John Luke, Florence, Lorenzo all wrote their congratulations and wishes for the happiness of the couple. Claire was quite content to be accused of playing Cupid and acknowledged herself "sold" on the married state. Besides this Claire had other good news of her own, she was bubbling over with happiness. She was pregnant again, and her letter was full of it.

"We are expecting a sister or brother for Melody in April, and both of us feel especially blessed that another life has been entrusted to our keeping. Somehow the feeling sick, headaches, blue spells, etc., don't matter too much when you realize what it will mean in our lives. Starting next week we are getting a maid to do the cleaning, because it is getting beyond my strength. Now that Michael is working regularly and making better money we can afford this luxury.

"I would like to wish all a very blessed and happy New

Year. By the time this reaches most of you the New Year will have run in. And Michael and I fondly hope it will bring in only the best for each and every one. Our little family has such a wonderful spirit, and I will especially pray for you all at Mass on the New Year.

"I must add one more item. We almost lost Vicky last month. She started bleeding, and an acute attack of an old kidney infection ran wild in my pup. It was touch and go for a week. She seems to be feeling better and now eats regularly. You can never know my feelings at the thought of losing my old friend. Vicky and I are so close, she is such a loyal friend—sick as she was, she guided me whenever the harness was put on and did a good job of it. She walks slowly now for her plump mummy, and is especially careful on steps. I think she knows somehow. I would hate to give her up—any time would be hard, but just now I feel I couldn't, when I depend on her so much. She is a dear hound and will rightly deserve a crown for her good deeds in dog heaven."

John Paul was glad for her and prayed that all would be well with her and the baby this time. Father S. was still very ill, but he wrote: "How very true to our true calling as members of CUSA we are proving to be. We are all laid up, some more, some less, but all are really true members of the wonderful apostolate of suffering according to the amount of grace His divine majesty imparts to each one of us. Prayer and suffering, oblation, consecration to Him, deeper and deeper love for Him, that is the life of a Cusan.

"What a wonderfully simple life God has entrusted u with. Accept His Holy Will and joyfully offer ourselves up to Him with resignation, with joy out of a deep, deep love for Him. What could be more simple, and yet what could be more beautiful?"

Lorenzo had especially joyful news, almost as good as Claire's, John Paul thought.

"I was glad to see the group letter, and here it is 4 P.M., and since 2 P.M. I've been trying to get going, but it seems everyone has picked today to telephone. Oh, well, I'll see what I can get done before something else comes up. I am sending along a clipping of a short trip I made to St. Francis House to meet Mary Ellen Kelly and other shut-ins. It was a great day for all of us, and I will never forget it. The sisters were really wonderful to us. I enjoyed your letter very much, and I'm sure if we could apply it without reservation to our life we could find a great happiness in a life even of pain and misfortune. Life everlasting is what will count, and I for one look forward to it and feel nothing in this world is worth living for. I am not saying this because I feel discontented. I sometimes wonder if it is because I am curious that I look forward to the day I will be so sick I'll know that the end is near, and that I will soon make the big change. I know this kind of talk offends some but I am sorry—as I know many people never like to give the future a thought. We all have our troubles, and if we learn to face them with faith—God gives us this for our own good—we would find life easier to bear. But it seems that as human beings we think more of what we have and want today than of the things we are promised. That is one human weakness we have to fight continually. I seem to have more trouble to write all the time and am looking forward to next month to see if I can do anything to help my muscles in my left side to relax, as I seem to have spasm there and very bad circulation.

"I do hope you are feeling better, Father. Florence, how lucky you are to get to read all those good books. I've had to cut my reading as my eyes are giving me trouble. Even

125

my hearing is going, so I guess I'm getting old. Claire, you sound very happy, and I hope all the problems of a mother will not be too complex for you to solve.

"Marge, it is good to hear you tell of getting out once more. Your new treatment seems to have done you much good. I hope it will continue to make you so well you can do even more.

"Lucille, I bet Dale and your other nieces and nephews are looking for Santa. Christmas won't be too much of an event here this year. We will look forward to another year. John Paul, may this coming year solve your problems. I've found that if we just wait, instead of making the move to solve it our way, something comes up to solve it for us in a way we never even thought of. I know, because after my mother died thirteen years ago I thought I would never be settled permanently again. I've been with my oldest sister since, and as long as health holds out I won't have to worry. Things we *really* need, instead of some things we want, I know God takes care of, and we worry needlessly.

"I have enclosed a paper to tell of my visit with Mary Ellen Kelly. I will leave it to the paper to tell the story."

The enclosure told about a happy day of Mass and prayer and of the comradeship between the shut-ins who had been able to attend. John Paul tried to think what a day like that would mean to someone who had never in this life expected to go outside or to Mass again, and the thought thrilled him with the joy of it. What had his life been like before Miss Grey had come into it? What had his first such day meant to him!

He rejoiced for Lorenzo and said a Magnificat of thanksgiving. That joy and thanksgiving did not decrease but became filled with an awed wonder when he learned next round that Lorenzo had died a few weeks after writing that letter.

"Well, old friend," he said to him in spirit, "you longed to know what was on the other side of the great change, and now you know. You looked forward to that day, and God would not keep you waiting longer."

His place in the group was taken by a young colored girl, Doris Thompson, who had just been discharged from a tuberculosis sanatorium. It was funny, John Paul did not even know until several rounds had passed that she was colored, so unimportant are things like that in CUSA. It didn't matter. They all welcomed her as a new friend. He liked what she said in one of her letters about work. "John Luke, I am glad you are able to work at your job at Catholic Charities. It grieves me to hear people complaining about their work or about having to work, etc. I guess I am full of the notion of work this round because some of the women I live with want work and can't get it because of their physical conditions; others hate their jobs and are ashamed of them because they are menial. There is so little under-standing in our modern world of what work is."

He agreed with what she said to Father, too: "Father, your letters are always just what the doctor ordered, and like his medicine are sometimes hard to take, though we know it's necessary. Isn't it queer that just to accept God's judgment and will and to believe in His love is often the hardest thing one can do? How many fall from grace just because of that, we can't even guess. I found that has been my greatest difficulty. Learning to accept God's will, judg-ment, preference, etc., rather than my own, and to trust His Providence and love."

Florence was still very busy and often had time only for

a short note, but in the same letter she too had commented on Father's message.

"I find special satisfaction in your letter this round. It helps to fill a void that developed in my life when I lost my hearing. With no sermons, retreats, missions, advice, the personal touch of a letter like yours seems to do more for me than a whole book of spiritual reading."

John Paul enjoyed his messages too, and said so. In fact sometimes he got inspiration for his answer to the question of the month in the leader's group letter from Father S.'s messages.

The leaders' group letters joined all the leaders of groups into a discussion group. A question was posed each month, deeply spiritual and wholly practical, which each leader answered as he liked. All the answers were collected, composed, discussed together with pertinent quotes from saints and theologians or from Our Lord Himself in regard to that question. The first chaplain of CUSA acted as moderator, and together with the "Mother Abbess" helped direct the discussions. Much was gained in this manner by all the leaders, and what they gained they in turn passed down to their "Families."

The question for one month was: "What are the principles—or the basis—of your own spiritual life? By what means—in what way—do we put them into practice in our daily life?"

"Mother Abbess," in posing the question, went on: "This seems a very intimate question to ask—especially as it should be answered in a very frank, personal way. Do not answer it by expressing what you have learned by spiritual reading or by the advice of your director, but what is really in your spiritual life, the fruit of your experiences, your thoughts, the work of the special grace of God in your soul.

"God works in as many different ways as there are different souls who are 'of the same family,' and I should not be surprised if it happens that quite a few of you say, after reading the answers to this new question: 'Really, this one or that one is actually a brother or sister soul of mine.' It would give you help, confidence, and a great joy. For some it might be the end of a feeling of isolation. But of course it means we should all be very simple, very selfless in answering. Let us try and do our best."

And they all did that because they had learned to speak to the others freely and joyfully. John Paul wrote: "The basis of my spiritual life is love, just a plain, ordinary guy's love that wants to do everything in such a way as to please the one he loves. I never had much of it myself, but when I began to learn something about the great love of Our Lord for me through my friend who writes for me, and to realize what that love meant, I was knocked out. I couldn't understand it, and I still can't. All I can do, all I do, is go on trying to love more to make up some part of the love God has for me by accepting all that comes to me with joy as His will, loving it because He sends it—crosses, joys, sorrows, all, everything."

He hoped he had expressed himself well enough for the other leaders to understand something of what he meant, but he wished he could have expressed better something of that fire which more and more consumed him in a wonderful warmth. But he knew mere words could not express it.

He enjoyed reading the other answers in the next round when the leader had summed up most of the answers.

"All I know," one leader had written, "is that I am so grateful for God's unspeakable goodness to me that I want to yield my will to His Divine Will in every way as completely and trustingly as a child yields to its mother's arms."

"Another leader describes himself as a dumbbell," the general leader said, "and then proceeds to speak of his own spiritual principles in a way that made me say to myself, 'May God grant us to meet many such . . . dumbbells. He tells us that the basic principle of his spiritual life is to seek union with God; to seek to know Him more, to seek to love Him more—to seek to serve Him more. I wish it would be possible to write all he has to say about these three different points. He ends by this, 'I am daily seeking union with Him, perfect union.' But he writes just before that ending: 'It is a real struggle, this fight to overcome monotony and the innate urging of the flesh and continue seeking that union with Him!'

"How well we understand what you mean, dear Bill! Lack of independence, the monotony of our daily lives, are two of the great crosses for us invalids," she agreed.

Two of the leaders had answers almost alike. One said: "My life is a book that God is writing, though sometimes I have interfered and spoiled a page." The other said: "My life is the story of graces not properly corresponded to."

Halfway through the letters, John Paul was struck by a sudden thought: in the leaders' group letter, the leaders were as simple and practical in discussing their handicaps and illnesses and their spiritual lives, and as matter-of-fact, as other people were about their businesses or professions. Their interior lives were not dress clothes for Sunday but plain, ordinary wear for everyday. He wondered how their letters would look to someone outside CUSA who knew none of its members. Would they marvel at the things Claire "saw" through her fingers, her ears, and especially through the eyes of her wonderful husband, Michael, and her faithful dog, Vicky? Would they marvel that she found time in a busy life of wife and homemaker for spiritual reading and study and meditation, and marvel that she should take time to share the results of these with her friends in CUSA?

Would it surprise them that Michael should take his promises not to hinder his wife's practice of her religion so seriously that he should be her eyes for reading to her the deeply spiritual books she wanted to read and did not have in Braille, as well as lighter reading for entertainment? Or would it seem natural to them, as it did to Claire and Michael, the way things ought to be for those who married in Christ?

Would they wonder at people like Harry and Therese whose thoughts and love reached out to the whole world, though they were physically bound to their beds? He wondered what they would think even of his own daily schedule. Up at five, to be washed and dressed by an orderly. Then a whole hour to lie there and think until breakfast, when he was propped up in his bed. After breakfast he got up in a wheel chair, and if he wanted, a book was propped on the stand in front of him for him to read until the physiotherapist came at ten. If he didn't feel like reading, he could sit there and think some more, looking out the window at the big lawn and trees and people passing by on the wide walks—patients, visitors, doctors, nurses, all the varied personnel who made up such a large institution. He could think of them, wonder about them, as perhaps many of them were wondering about him or others like him, perhaps at times envying them in their ease, even as they perhaps at times envied these others in their activity.

At 11:30 he had his face washed again, and an orderly gave him his lunch. After that was a two-hour rest period, and he went to bed again. Sometimes he listened to the radio; sometimes he slept.

At three or four o'clock he was up again, and sometimes he went out-doors in a wheel chair till supper time. In the wintertime, when it got dark so early, he went out on the sun porch and watched the men less handicapped play checkers. He liked to talk to them there, when he was feeling good, and sometimes he played a game of checkers himself, another man being his hands. Some of the men smoked out there then, hungrily, because that was often their first smoke of the day, since that was the only place in the hospital where smoking was allowed. Of course, those who could help themselves more, often wheeled themselves to the lavatory and smoked there, and some even smoked in bed. The nurses and orderlies would raise hell about that, though, if one caught a fellow doing it. It was too dangerous. But most of them closed their eyes to the illicit smoking that went on in the lavatory and never said anything unless a supervisor or fire inspector happened around.

John Paul thought of these things as he read the letters of the Cusan leaders, each giving the basis of his or her own spiritual life. One said love; another, resignation; another, hope. And another said that gratitude to God for His generosity was the foundation for his own interior life. Many leaders, many answers, many thoughts behind them all, as there were many stories behind the illnesses or handicaps of them all. Some were born crippled or blind or deaf, some had become so as a child or an adult through disease; some had met with violent accidents in the course of work or play. Some, though sick at present, looked forward to better health in a year or two or more, even perhaps eventually to a real cure. But all were characterized by their spirit of hopeful abandonment to God's providence and determination to use the crosses which might have crushed them.

John Paul went on with the letters:

Therese, another leader, wrote: "It is difficult to put down on paper the basis of one's spiritual life—especially for a fledgling like myself—but with the help of the Holy Ghost, I'll give it a whirl.

"I'm a Franciscan Tertiary, and, as such, have our Third Order rule to guide daily life in a great measure. To me all seems to be bound up in attaining an ever more perfect resignation to the Divine Will. In daily life, I find things at every turn to help me acquire this. They are not spectacular things—mostly they are the little day-to-day things that happen to all of us. In other words, learning to live so that nothing can fluster me—to live calmly in that big item, 'trust'—to turn everything I stumble on, even though it may be untoward to an extreme, into some good.

"To my mind, one of the greatest things God did for us to help us until that day of our resurrection was to give us Our Lord in the Holy Eucharist. I've always had a special Friend in the Blessed Sacrament, and since my illness, I've become increasingly grateful for the doctrine of the Indwelling of the Holy Spirit. This, in particular, I think has been one of the biggest factors of help for me. His presence there in the soul of one who doesn't even deserve existence gives ample food for contemplation. That contemplation is most often humbling. His presence there presents almost unlimited occasions to love. Because He is there I can talk to Him on those occasions when I would like to scream at something or somebody.

"But in spite of all the help at my command, the picture does not always appear in such rosy hues. I find often that, even to accomplish the minimum I manage, it takes a forcing —a brute forcing on occasion—of the will (and how many times that brute force just keeps eluding me!). It is then that I am most thankful for the union of prayer that is ours in CUSA."

And Harry said: "The big question of the month has really stumped me. I don't have the skill with words necessary to say what I feel. But I can tell you in the simple language of my childhood how I was taught to live. From the time I could walk it was perfectly common to wander into the village chapel in Ireland—to go up and sit down on the steps leading to the Communion rail—and tell Himself about what I'd been up to. When I left, if you'd seen me make an airy motion at the holy water fount by the door —I wasn't making a sloppy Sign of the Cross—I was really waving good-bye to Him! The Boy of Nazareth was a school Friend—and I was taught not to do anything I would be ashamed to do were He with me as He was in His Boyhood. When I couldn't run over the hills any more—the Boy came and sat with me until I'd let rebellion and hatred drive Him away. I'd gladly help carry my piece of His cross until my anger and impatience would make Him take my burden. Anger, temper, impatience—these are my besetting sins— what my grandmother called my 'cow-sins.' She said I was like a cow who would give a fine bucket of milk then lift her feet and kick it over. My constant struggle is not to kick.

"I think my simple, childish reasoning is a boyish version of the Indwelling our Therese talks of. Always living with the consciousness that He is with me always—(that last should have been *all* ways)."

John Paul liked this. If one can think like this, one could realize that nothing, not our weakness, our faults nor even our sins can lead to despair if we think Whose temples we are. On the contrary, one sees the glory of God's Presence

134

in us helping us to do good and overcome evil, and making us sorry for the evil we have done, even using it to humble us and draw us closer to Himself. And in this realization is inspiration, consolation and hope.

He went to the last letter, which was that of "Mother Abbess" herself, who asked no revelation of experiences from her leaders which she would not make herself. She wrote, "I, also, dear friends, think that all my life should be a hymn of gratitude to Our Lord, for the graces He has showered on me. That gratitude will be, I am sure, the theme of my song through eternity, and I am also sure that I shall then be thanking God even with more grateful wonder for the trials and sorrows of life, for the honor to have been invited by Him to bear a part of His Cross, than for any joy of this world.

"To love God and be a help, an occasion for others to come to love Him, is my greatest wish. That love is His most beautiful gift to His creatures. 'The love of God has been poured into my soul by His Holy Spirit that lives in me'—'It is not you who have chosen me,' says Christ. We have, I find, to keep very close, very near and united to Him, so as to be always ready to receive this gift of love. And how marvelous it is to think that we can be the means for many other souls to discover also the treasure of that love! We need not hustle or preach, or do anything striking: the silent, humble offerings will work wonders about which we shall perhaps know nothing in this world. What beautiful discoveries we are going to make when arriving in heaven! How many unknown but very grateful and loving friends we should meet."

In another round they discussed the doctrine of the Mystical Body in their lives. One leader, Margaret C., wrote: "Suffering itself alone avails us nothing. God requires that

we accept and bear it willingly as our share in the Divine
Plan of redemption; as St. Paul says, "to fill up what is
missing in the Passion of Christ, for His Body, the Church
. . . may the most Blessed Trinity, in infinite mercy, forgive
any deficit for which we may be held accountable in this
marvelous traffic (sharing one another's graces) which
Jesus, when coming of age, referred to as 'my Father's busi-
ness.' " And another, Justine, gave an answer very like it:
"We the members of the Church Militant on earth, along
with the Church Triumphant in heaven, which is the saints,
and the Suffering Church of purgatory, form the Mystical
Body of Christ, with Christ as our Head. We pray to the
saints in heaven, who in turn intercede for us before the
throne of God. By our suffering we fill up those things that
are wanting in the Mystical Body of Christ. We share the
merits of our suffering with the less fortunate ones (our job
is an immense one—we can almost say that we are carrying
the world on our shoulders). As the heart pumps the blood
through the body to keep it alive, we by our suffering can
circulate the graces through the Mystical Body for the
sanctification of souls."

Miss Grey commented on the similarity of the two answers and said, by way of explanation, to John Paul: "Not
that there is really anything wanting in the Passion of Christ
itself, for His redemption of us is complete. It is a great
mystery, but somehow in His love He has permitted us a
share in His life, His whole life, including His Passion, so
that in a very special sense we can say truthfully that Our
Lady is Co-redemptrix, and all we her children, in a lesser
sense, are co-redeemers, too. God permits us a share in paying off our own debt, not by ourselves but through our
life in the Mystical Body, which is the life of His Son. We
can meditate on that and learn a lot from it, but we can't

understand it. God's love is beyond our reason and our understanding. We can just be grateful for it."

Grace said: "We can compare the Mystical Body in relation to the human body especially in its reaction to an ill affecting a member of it. The entire healthy part of human organism rushes to aid the afflicted part, and helps it in any way possible—so should we of the Mystical Body rush to the aid of ailing members. This is brought home to the Cusan very clearly in our Patron, Motto and Intention idea. Who could be "sicker" than those benefiting by our prayers—the Communists in Russia and China, the materialists of our country, etc.? And just as the human body fights to prevent illness, we try to gain the sanctification of priests, vocations, etc., to prevent ills in the Mystical Body. Certainly our having a patron for each group shows our belief in the Communion of Saints . . . for we are actually prayers to the Blessed in heaven (the Church Triumphant) to help us to gain graces for the Church Militant on earth as well as the Church Suffering in purgatory. It is this very doctrine of the Mystical Body which causes me to wonder why everyone is not engaged in some kind of apostolic work for the Church . . . the kind that best suits them as persons, to be sure . . . but *some* kind of activity to show their awareness of their responsibility to the rest of the Church. It may only be in the form of living a perfect housewife's life and offering up sacrifices for apostolic intentions, while teaching one's children love for the faith . . . and a *living* awareness of the role we all have to play in the sanctification of not only ourselves, but the whole world."

Another leader wrote: "If we think about it, it fills us with a wonderful sense of awe, this Unity. We are never really alone. The prayers of others help us, our prayers, works, suffering, help ourselves and each other; our sins, failings, omissions hurt ourselves and each other. Because of this, we are no longer free to do or not to do good; to love or not to love; we have the obligation to let the action and love of Christ flow through us in whatever way He wills. We cannot be unconcerned about the problems and pains of people next door or across the street or across the world. We share the same *life*, at least potentially, and are nourished by the same nourishment. All our sufferings take on meaning, if we consider these things, all take on grandeur even, and a certain splendor of being. We can no more now be uncaring about the most depraved, the most sinful, the most base and ugly, than my hand can be uncaring about the gangrene of my foot. We are the same Body! If we meditated every moment of our lives and lived a hundred years, we could not begin to understand the greatness and splendor of this reality!"

Another leader's answer was shorter but just as thoughtful: "We who are privileged to suffer can honor God, say our prayers, etc., better than those who are busily employed every day. It was by suffering that God redeemed the world. There is so much evil in the world that about the only remedy we can find, next to the grace of God, is the patient suffering of so many good people. We must never be discouraged, therefore, but realize we are doing a very important work for humanity!"

As winter passed into spring again, John Paul was more and more confined to bed, but he rejoiced to see the others, like Florence, keeping busy doing things to help others to live more completely and happily.

Margie was feeling better, so she had strong hopes that the new drug she was taking was helping her. Her children were doing fine too, and she wrote of interesting or funny things that happened at school. Father S., of course, knew that his time was limited, but waited patiently for God's will to be accomplished in him. Lucille was gay and joyous as ever, always sending along a verse she had written, and some, John Paul knew, were good. They grew better, too, as she wrote more. Dorothy soon found a warm place in their hearts, and they all rejoiced with her as she began working again at the work she loved as a city welfare-worker, after her health returned to normal.

John Luke was always full of fun and kept them laughing in his letters even when he sometimes gave someone a gentle little "lecture." In a short while they were all calling him "Pop-Pop," as his little grandchildren did. He never complained of his heart, but in one letter he exclaimed: "It's funny how we change! I always loved noise and excitement. Now my battered heart craves a few days of quiet. I'll be sixty-three in September, and feeling much better in the hands of a new doctor. I couldn't wish an enemy a heart attack—it's terrible." Another time he wrote—and John Paul had a good laugh at that because it ended happily, after all—"a month ago, I died of a heart attack. When I opened my eyes the priest had given me Extreme Unction, and my family was at my bedside. I am still here."

In April Claire's baby was born and lived four hours. They called him Michael David. There was no hope for him. But Michael got permission for Claire to hold him afterward.

"I felt great peace at holding this angel baby and feel this was the first grace my son got for me. There were no tears, but gratitude that I could see my baby and hold him and know he was safe from this world's sorrows forever."

He was an R.H. baby, owing to a mix-up in transfusions

twenty years before, when R.H. positive blood had been given to Claire. Now she and Michael knew they could never have a living child, unless science discovered some new miracle to overcome this problem. "Due to the difficult time I had, the doctor feels we should never have more." Claire went on: "But I hold fast to the Catholic belief that God knows best. If this is to be our life, then somehow, somewhere I will get the strength to face what is ahead of us. I thank God for Michael, and this new cross has only drawn us closer. I feel Michael's namesake will take his hand and help lead him one day to the altar with me."

In the next round, there seemed some hope for that, too . . . Claire wrote: "I know our angel children are praying for their daddy. He is going to take a course in religion this fall. He is interested in the Faith and has always said he would become a Catholic. However, I have never forced the issue. We talk openly about religion and he feels as much a Catholic as I do, only I told him it is something you have to be before you can fully appreciate it. I hope this fresh interest will lead to a fervent desire to embrace the Faith. He is considering going to St. Joseph's College, which is run by the Jesuits. It is only four blocks from where we live. I am planning to take up something else this Fall. Both of us need new interests and something else to think about. The days are so empty for me at times, and I am sure schooling of some kind will perk us up and give us a new look at things. Until an adoption or something else comes up we have to content ourselves with living without a family. . . . . You know, it isn't the height to a mountain climber, it is the pebble in his shoe. . . . And that pretty well sums up how I am just now—trying to get along with the daily routine—doing without the thing I yearn for most—by trying to live each day and better prepare myself for motherhood if the opportunity presents itself—God willing it will some day. Father, I especially want you to remember us when you can think of it. A little mention in your prayers at Mass will be so appreciated. Married people of today have so many problems facing them at times. I am sure you understand—you must see so many cases in your parish.

"Vicky is getting well and we are taking her over tonight for a checkup. She is a dear animal but isn't too keen on work just now. We have been confined too long, and it is reflected in the dog. She is still capable but her nerves are bad—she feels we are safer at home and would rather not go out. I am hoping to work her out of it so we can get out more. Both of us will rust out if we don't get busy soon."

John Paul did not write much that summer. The heat was too much for his dwindling strength. Miss Grey and Gregory worried about him, and he was sorry for the pain he caused them. As fall and winter came, he felt a little better, and was able to write a long letter to welcome the new chaplain, when Father S. died. The new chaplain was really good and a worthy successor to him. He was not sick but had suffered from some pulmonary trouble. He was now well and teaching at a seminary. He wrote them: "It was a tonic to read your letter and to see how cheerfully busy everyone had been. You know, despite our physical limitations, if we can only keep pegging away at our work enthusiastically, steadily doing what our strength allows, we will discover that in the long run we will accomplish just as much as anyone else. Those of us so confined as to be immobile have their work cut out for them just as definitely as we active souls. They must bear their particular burdens of pain, of helplessness, of feelings of inadequacy—they must face each new day of 'work' wholly confident that they can accomplish just as much as the rest of us, and often more!)

("But enthusiasm, joy, must be there. Where do we get it? From realizing that *we are in Christ—we are His Body*. When we work, live, suffer, worry, He lives, works, worries and suffers in us. We help Him give glory and worship to the Father and *save the world.*)

"We fill up in our bodies and in all our lives the measure of suffering that Christ left for us; we glory in our infirmities, for they show forth the power and dominion of God in us. We are alive—no, we aren't alive—Christ is alive in us. (How can we Christians not live our lives with holy enthusiasm? And our limitations and sufferings—how can we not be happy about them if He wants them so?

"Put everything into the hands of God—live as He has ordained, be joyful in spending each day working for Him.")

He had a sense of humor too, as again he wrote: "The month of September spells the end of vacation for us teaching folks. In a few short days our peace will be shattered by the arrival of 281 youngsters taking their first steps toward the priesthood. That noble ideal doesn't seem to make them any less human (or noisy). We are grateful for many acres of playground and a magnificent swimming pool where they can pour out some of their liveliness and spirit after a day of class and study, otherwise the place could not contain them."

In December Claire had wonderful news. John Paul cried, and so did Miss Grey. She said Gregory wasn't far from it, though manlike he denied it.

"Our prayers were answered sooner than we had hoped," she told them. "We got ourselves a fine baby boy on the feast of the Immaculate Conception when he was only five days old. We are so thrilled and grateful for having him. He is a good baby but requires lots of care right now, and with the new house we have been up to our ears in work and nervous strain. Please all say a prayer with us in thanksgiving. We hope to legally adopt Christopher Francis by February or March. We had him baptized Sunday. Chris suits him, and I will send a picture in the next group letter."

When Miss Grey finished answering that letter for him, John Paul was smiling. The smile still lingered on his face when she had gone again, and on through supper and afterward when the new orderly came to turn off the lights. He looked out the window. It was raining again, a thin, steady drizzle that would freeze later and was icy cold now. It was a dreary night—all blackness and clouds with a faint reddish haze over part of the sky. Somehow the night reminded him of that other one, long ago, when he had been lying at another window exactly like this, filled with blackness and despair and hatred for life and the living. A lot had happened since then, and often he felt as if that other had been some other person, almost unknown to himself. He thought of his friends, especially of Claire and her newfound joy. He thought of Father C. and Father S., of Lorenzo and Jerry, and of those other babies Claire called her "angel children." They had found joy too, a different kind of joy from Claire's but really a better one, because it was forever and had no pain or sorrow in it. He said prayers for the priests and Lorenzo because only God knows the disposition of a soul, but in his own heart he did not doubt they had found not more pain but joy in union with God when they made the great change Lorenzo had talked about.

And now the rain kept coming down, and it was as if it washed the last trace of bitterness, bewilderment and rebellion away and left him, somehow, clean. God's will is in all things, and God's plan—he could see it now . . . And laced through the plan, lighting it and shining through it, was God's love; and its end: heaven—not the Golden City of the materialists nor the dreamless Nirvana of the idealists, but union with God, the consummation of the soul's betrothal to Him for all eternity. Nothing else mattered but that: everything fitted into that plan, pain, comfort, happiness, sorrow, fear, triumph, there was nothing lost, nothing lacking. Suffering had taken from him all things men dream of, yet given him back more than men hope for; it was his own path to heaven. For him there could be no other.

"All the way to heaven is heaven," St. Catherine had said . . . For He said: "I am the Way." Miss Grey had read it to him one day long ago. At last he understood—and the understanding thrilled him with a joy too great to be borne. Thinking of these things, John Paul smiled to himself and was almost asleep when the nurse stopped by his bed.

"John Paul, Father Coleman is here for confessions," she told him. "Tomorrow is First Friday, you know. Do you want to see him? If so, I'll straighten your bed a bit."

John Paul turned his smile on her. "Sure," he replied. "I want to receive tomorrow for something real special. I want to learn to be patient with my own self, my own state, and my own prayer. Do you know, Miss Long, that that is a hard thing to do?"

She smiled in return. "I sure do, John Paul. I guess it is because we know ourselves so well. But now let me straighten your bed and fix you up real nice for Father's visit."

Father Coleman was friendly, and though John Paul knew he actually was very busy and pressed for time, the priest somehow gave the impression that he had all the time in the world just to listen to John Paul's confession and his troubles, and help him with them.

When John Paul told him about his prayer, he said: "I wouldn't worry about that at all, John Paul. We don't pray in order to feel good or happy or even holy. We pray to please God, to glorify Him and give Him some part of the worship which is His due. So be at peace in these things. Often we are closest to God when we feel farthest away, especially when we are trying our best and conscious of no serious infidelity to Him."

After Father Coleman had gone, John Paul went to sleep almost at once and slept well until morning when the orderly came to make him ready for the day.

"You are very pale, John Paul; don't you feel well?" he asked solicitously, noting the grayish tinge of his patient's face and the quick, short breathing.

"No, not so well this morning," John Paul answered him.

The nurse came and looked at John Paul. "I'm going to call Doctor Woods to come over," she told him. "You take it easy, John Paul."

She had been gone only a few moments when Father Coleman came. John Paul welcomed him with his Visitor with eagerness, love and a great thanksgiving. After Father Coleman had gone, he lay there thinking of this Visitor. His body was very tired and felt heavy, and there was in it a new pain. But his mind was at peace and he was content. He closed his eyes and smiled, thinking.

A short time later the nurse came to the door and looked in to tell him Doctor Woods was on his way. Seeing the smile, and his eyes closed, she said to herself: "He's asleep now. I won't waken him until the doctor comes."

If she had come closer she would have seen that John Paul was asleep indeed. But it was the long sleep from which he would waken only in eternity.

X.   Epilogue

Margie and John Filan have since died, and may all who have grown to know and love them in these pages pray for their souls and for all members of CUSA. Lucille is feeling better these days, and still closes her letters with a gay verse from her Cozyhill home about the earth, the wind, the trees, the ducks, all the cozy things of home. Florence had to resign from CUSA because of the pressure of so much work, but she still remembers her friends in CUSA prayerfully, as they remember her, and she hopes some day to join us again when circumstances permit. She continues now her work with those handicapped by deafness, understanding their problem as few workers can because it has also been her own. Claire lost another baby girl, Madonna. But in a recent letter she wrote: "Father, both Michael and I thoroughly enjoyed your message in this recent letter. Grace is a powerful thing, and speaking from experience, I know the full power of it in my life. Michael and I are grateful that Madonna lived for Baptism too. That in itself was the biggest answer to prayer I ever saw. I am feeling so much better now and happy to report Chris is now legally ours. The hearing was September 20th, and the judge awarded him to us without any difficulty. Chris speaks for himself by his chubby cheeks and smiling face. He squealed Dada all the time while there. Our doctor that got him for us appeared, as did the baby doctor and visiting nurse, to testify that I was capable and able to care for Chris. It was a wonderful moment to hear him legally declared our son.

"Another tremendous answer to prayer took place September 18th and 19th. Michael became a Catholic on September 18th and made his first Holy Communion the following morning. Believe me, it was one of the happiest moments of my life to have my beloved husband kneel beside me at the altar rail and receive our Blessed Lord. Our union was made complete then. I am so thankful I couldn't begin to express in words what I felt.

"I am going to beg your prayers for another big thing. Please pray God's will is done in this matter and that all concerned will be directed. We have applied for another baby. I thought one would come along in about a year (we asked for a girl), but the director of Catholic Charities, Father Marley, sent a nun out here to tell us of a child that they have and to see if we would be interested in him. Robert is fourteen months, blind, and in great need of training and love. Both Michael and I immediately said we would take him if all else is well with the boy. I went to see him and found he couldn't sit up yet or talk. The little youngster doesn't know how to hold a toy yet, either. He was with a couple from a week old, and when they discovered he was blind, they gave him to Charities. He was eight months old then—and he has been sitting or lying in a crib ever since. Of course it means a tremendous amount on me. I sometimes think I may not hold up to it. Robert will require so much care. However, we feel he won't be taken by most couples, and if we don't give him a home he'll never have a chance. Being either blind or an orphan is bad enough—but being both is something we can't overlook for his sake. Financially we can't afford it right now, but

Michael feels things will work out if we get him. Chris is so advanced for his ten and a half months, and to see this little baby, thin, unable to sit, only aware of his thumb which he never parts company with, just breaks your heart. After a more thorough checkup by specialists to make sure there is nothing else the matter with him, we can see what can be done. The opportunity is a wonderful one! It isn't our girl that we wanted, but it is a concrete way to offer thanks to God for our blessings by helping one of His little orphaned souls. After all, we want children, and it doesn't really matter what or who they are, or even what is the matter with them. If we can help them, that is the primary thing. Please pray we are guided in this matter. It will be a tremendous undertaking. I pray my health and strength can measure up to it. I'll keep you posted on how it turns out."

So Claire has gained both strength and courage through her sufferings, which she passes on to all members of her groups, as do the other Cusans. May God continue His blessings upon her and all members of CUSA and teach us to bear our suffering well.

Helen Caldwell Day was born in Marshall, Texas in 1926; she became a Catholic while a student nurse in New York, and returned to the South to found a house of hospitality in Memphis patterned after that of Dorothy Day's Catholic Worker. In addition to this book, Miss Day has written COLOR EBONY, the autobiography of her first 23 years, and NOT WITHOUT TEARS, the story of the founding and development of the Blessed Martin House. In 1955 she married Jesse Riley and now is learning to be a housekeeper.